The History of Merlin and King Arthur

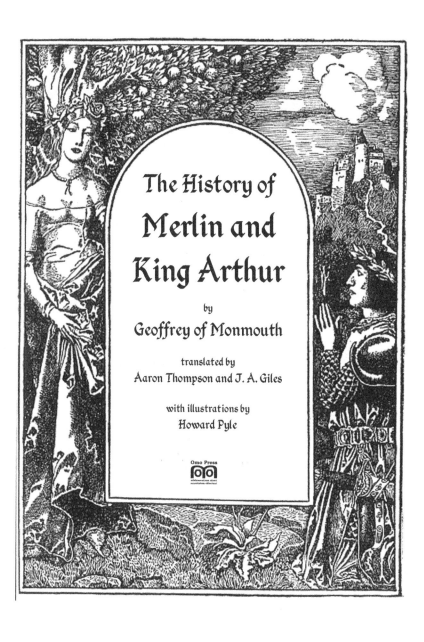

The History of
Merlin and
King Arthur

by
Geoffrey of Monmouth

translated by
Aaron Thompson and J. A. Giles

with illustrations by
Howard Pyle

Omo Press

Cover illustration:
James Archer, La Mort d'Arthur, 1860 (large detail)

Interior illustrations are from Howard Pyle's four books about Arthurian
legends

The Middle Ages had little sense of history and imagined that Arthur
and his knights looked like medieval knights in armor. In fact, since
the stories of Arthur occur just after the Romans left Britain, we
would expect them to wear chain mail, like late Roman cavalry.
Nevertheless, this book includes Pyle's illustrations of knights in
armor, since Geoffrey of Monmouth himself lived in the Middle Ages
and probably shared the medieval view.

ISBN 978-1-941667-02-6

Contents

Epistle Dedicatory

To Robert Earl of Gloucester.

Whilst occupied on many and various studies, I happened to light upon the History of the Kings of Britain, and wondered that in the account which Gildas and Bede, in their elegant treatises, had given of them, I found nothing said of those kings who lived here before the Incarnation of Christ, nor of Arthur, and many others who succeeded after the Incarnation; though their actions both deserved immortal fame, and were also celebrated by many people in a pleasant manner and by heart, as if they had been written.

Whilst I was intent upon these and such like thoughts, Walter, archdeacon of Oxford, a man of great eloquence, and learned in foreign histories, offered me a very ancient book in the British tongue, which, in a continued regular story and elegant style, related the actions of them all, from Brutus the first king of the Britains, down to Cadwallader the son of Cadwallo. At his request, therefore, though I had not made fine language my study, yet contented with my own homely style, I undertook the translation of that book into Latin. For if I had swelled the pages with rhetorical flourishes, I must have tired my readers, by employing their attention more upon my words than upon the history.

To you, therefore, Robert Earl of Gloucester, this work humbly sues for the favour of being so corrected by your advice, that it may not be thought to be the poor offspring of Geoffrey of Monmouth, but when polished by your refined wit and judgment, the production of him who had Henry the glorious king of England for his father, and whom we see an accomplished scholar and philosopher, as well as a brave soldier and expert commander.

Chapter 1: The Saxon Invasion

King Constantine

After the Romans left Britain,[1] the two leaders, Guanius and Melga, issued forth from their ships, in which they had fled over into Ireland, and with their band of Scots, Picts, Norwegians, Dacians, and others, whom they had brought along with them, seized upon all Albania as far as the very wall. Understanding likewise that the Romans were gone, never to return any more, they, now, in a more insolent manner than before, began their devastations in the island.

Hereupon, Guithelin, archbishop of London, passed over into Lesser Britain,[2] called then Armorica, or Letavia, to desire assistance of their brethren. At that time Aldroen

---

[1] The Romans left Britain in about the year 410 AD.
[2] The French province of Brittany.

reigned there. This prince, seeing a prelate of so great dignity arrive, received him with honour, and inquired after the occasion of his coming. To whom Guithelin: —

"Your majesty can be no stranger to the misery which we your Britons, have suffered (which may even demand your tears), for against us the poor remains of the British race, all the people of the adjacent islands have risen up, and made an utter devastation in our country. For the Romans are tired of us, and have absolutely refused their assistance. So that now, deprived of all other hope we come to implore your clemency, that you would furnish us with forces, and protect a kingdom, which is of right your own, from the incursions of barbarians. For who but yourself ought, without your consent, to wear the crown of Constantine and Maximian, since the right your ancestors had to it is now devolved upon you? Prepare your fleet, and go with me. Behold! I deliver the kingdom of Britain into your hands."

To this Aldroen made answer: "There was a time formerly when I would not have refused to accept the island of Britain, if it had been offered me; for I do not think there was anywhere a more fruitful country while it enjoyed peace and tranquility. But now, since the calamities that have befallen it, it is become of less value, and odious both to me and all other princes. Nevertheless, out of respect to the right that my ancestors for many generations have had to your islands I deliver to you my brother Constantine with two thousand men, that with the good providence of God, he may free your country from the inroads of barbarians, and obtain the crown from himself; for indeed a larger number I do not mention to you, because I am daily threatened with disturbance from the Gauls."

He had scarcely done speaking before the archbishop returned him thanks, and when Constantine was called in, broke out into these expressions of joy: "Christ conquers; Christ commands; Christ reigns: behold the king of desolate Britain! Be Christ only present, and behold our defence, our hope and joy." In short, the ships being got ready, the men who were chosen out from all parts of the kingdom, were delivered to Guithelin.

When they had made all necessary preparations, they embarked, and arrived at the port of Totness; and then without delay assembled together the youth that was left in the island, and encountered the enemy; over whom, by the merit of the holy prelate, they obtained the victory. After this the Britons, before dispersed, flocked together from all parts, and in a council held at Silchester, promoted Constantine to the throne, and there performed the ceremony of his coronation.

They also married him to a lady, descended from a noble Roman family, whom archbishop Guithelin had educated and by whom the king had afterwards three sons, Constans, Aurelius Ambrosius, and Uther Pendragon. Constans, who was the eldest, he delivered to the church of Amphibalus in Winchester, that he might there take upon him the monastic order. But the other two, Aurelius and Uther, he committed to the care of Guithelin for their education.

At last, after ten years were expired, there came a certain Pict, who had entered in his service, and under pretence of holding some private discourse with him, in a nursery of young trees where nobody was present, stabbed him with a dagger.

Vortigern's Treachery

Upon the death of Constantine, a dissention arose among the nobility, about a successor to the throne. Some were for setting up Aurelius Ambrosius; others Uther Pendragon; others again some other persons of the royal family.

At last, when they could come to no conclusion, Vortigern, king of the Gewisseans, who was himself very ambitious of the crown, went to Constans the monk, and thus addressed himself to him:

"You see your father is dead, and your brothers on account of their age are incapable of government; neither do I see any of your family besides yourself, whom the people out to promote to the kingdom. If you will therefore follow my advice, I will, on condition of your increasing my private estate, dispose the people to favour your advancement, and free you from that habit, notwithstanding that it is against the rule of your order."

Constans, overjoyed at the proposal, promised, with an oath, that upon these terms he would grant him whatever he would desire.

Then Vortigern took him, and investing him in his regal habiliments, conducted him to London, and made him king, though not with the free consent of the people. Archbishop Guithelin was then dead, nor was there any other than durst perform the ceremony of his unction, on account of his having quitted the monastic order.

However, this proved no hindrance to his coronation, for Vortigern himself performed the ceremony instead of a bishop.

Constans, being thus advanced, committed the whole government of the kingdom to Vortigern, and surrendered himself up so entirely to his counsels, that he did nothing without his order. His own incapacity for government obliged him to do this, for he had learned any thing else rather than state affairs within his cloister.

Vortigern became sensible of this, and therefore began to deliberate with himself what course to take to obtain the crown, of which he had been before extremely ambitious. He saw that now was his proper time to gain his end easily, when the kingdom was wholly entrusted to his management; and Constans, who bore the title of king, was no more than the shadow of one, for he was of soft temper, a bad judge in matters of right, and not in the least feared, either by his own people, or by the neighbouring states. And as for his two bothers, Uther Pendragon and Aurelius Ambrosius, they were only children in their cradles, and therefore incapable of the government. All the older persons of the nobility were dead, so that Vortigern seemed to be the only man surviving that had craft, policy, and experience in matters of state; and all the rest in a manner children, or raw youths, who only inherited the honours of their parents and relations that had been killed in the former wars.

Vortigern, finding a concurrence of so many favourable circumstances, contrived how he might easily and cunningly depose Constans the monk, and immediately establish himself in his place. But in order to do this, he waited until he had first well established his power and interest in several countries. He therefore petitioned to have the king's treasures, and his fortified cities, in his own custody; pretending there was a rumour that the neighbouring islanders designed an invasion of the kingdom. This being granted him, he placed his own creatures in those cities, to secure them for himself.

Then having formed a scheme how to execute his treasonable designs, he went to the king and represented to him the necessity of augmenting the number of his domestics, that he might more safely oppose the invasion of the enemy, saying, "I am informed that the Picts are going to bring the Dacians and Norwegians in upon us, with a design to give us very great annoyance. I would therefore advise that you maintain some Picts in your court, who may do you good service among those of that nation. For if it is true that they are preparing to begin a rebellion, you may employ them as spies upon their countrymen in their plots and stratagems, so as easily to escape them."

This was the dark treason of a secret enemy; for he did not recommend this out of regard for the safety of Constans, but because he knew the Picts to be a giddy people, and ready for all manner of wickedness; so that, in a fit of drunkenness or passion, they might easily be incensed against the king, and make no scruple to assassinate him.

He despatched messengers into Scotland, with an invitation to a hundred Pictish soldiers, whom accordingly he received into the king's household; and when admitted, he showed them more respect than all the rest of the domestics, by making them several presents, and allowing them a luxurious table, insomuch as they looked upon him as the king. So great was the regard they had for him, that they made songs of him about the streets, the subject of which was, that Vortigern deserved the government, deserved the sceptre of Britain; but that Constans was unworthy of it.

This encouraged Vortigern to show them still more favour, and when by these practices he had made them entirely his creatures, he took an opportunity, when they were drunk, to tell them that he was going to retire out of Britain, to see if he could get a better estate; for the small revenue he had then, he said, would not so much as enable him to maintain a retinue of fifty men. Then putting on a look of sadness, he withdrew to his own apartment, and left them drinking in the hall. The Picts, murmuring, said to one another, "Why do we suffer this monk to live? Why do we not kill him, that Vortigern may enjoy his crown? Who is so fit to succeed as he? A man so generous to us is worthy to rule, and deserves all the honour and dignity that we can bestow upon him."

After this, breaking into Constans' bed-chamber, they fell upon him and killed him, and carried his head to Vortigern. At the sight of it, he put on a mournful countenance, and burst forth into tears, though at the same time he was almost transported with joy. However, he summoned together the citizens of London (for there the act was committed), and commanded all the assassins to be bound, and their heads to be cut off for this abominable parricide. In the meantime there were some who had a suspicion, that this piece of villainy was wholly the contrivance of Vortigern, and the Picts were only his instruments to execute it. Others again as positively asserted his innocence. At last the matter being left in doubt, those who had the care of the two brothers, Aurelius Ambrosius and Uther Pendragon, fled over with them into Lesser Britain, for fear of being killed by Vortigern. There they were kindly received by king Budes, who took care to give them an education suitable to their royal birth.

Now Vortigern, seeing nobody to rival him in the kingdom, placed the crown on his own head, and thus gained the pre-eminence over all the rest of the princes. At last his treason being discovered, the people of the adjacent islands, whom the Picts had brought into Albania, made insurrection against him. For the Picts were enraged on account of the death of their fellow soldiers, who had been slain for the murder of Constans, and endeavoured to revenge that injury upon him.

Vortigern therefore was daily in great distress, and lost a considerable part of his army in a war with them. He had likewise no less trouble from another quarter, for fear of Aurelius Ambrosius, and his brother Uther Pendragon, who, as we said before, had fled, on his account, into Lesser Britain. For he heard it rumoured, day after day, that they had now arrived at man's estate, and had built a vast fleet, with a design to return back to the kingdom, which was their undoubted right.

Saxons Arrive

In the meantime there arrived in Kent three bringandines, or long galleys, full of armed men, under the command of two brothers, Horsa and Hengist. Vortigern was then at Dorobernia, now Canterbury, which city he used often to visit; and being informed of the arrival of some tall strangers in large ships, he ordered that they should be received peaceably, and conducted into his presence. As soon as they were brought before him, he cast his eyes upon the two brothers, who excelled all the rest both in nobility and gracefulness of person; and having taken a view of the whole company, asked them of what country they were, and what was the occasion of their coming into his kingdom. To whom Hengist (whose years and wisdom entitled him to precedence), in the name of the rest, made the following answer:—

"Most noble king, Saxony, which is one of the countries of Germany, was the place of our birth; and the occasion of our coming was to offer our service to you or some other prince. For we were driven out of our native country, for no other reason, but that the laws of the kingdom required it. It is customary among us, that when we come to be overstocked with people, our princes from all the provinces meet together, and command all the youths of the kingdom to assemble before them; then casting lots they make choice of the strongest and ablest of them, to go into foreign nations, to procure themselves a subsistence, and free their native country from a superfluous multitude of people. Us two brothers, Hengist and Horsa, they made generals over them, out of respect to our ancestors, who enjoyed the same honour. In obedience, therefore, to the laws so long established, we put out to sea, and under the good guidance of Mercury have arrived in your kingdom."

The king, at the name of Mercury, looking earnestly upon them, asked them what religion they professed. "We worship," replied Hengist, "our country's gods, Saturn and Jupiter, and the other deities that govern the world, but especially Mercury, whom in our language we call Woden, and to whom our ancestors consecrated the fourth day of the week, still called after his name Wodensday. Next to him we worship the powerful goddess, Frea, to whom they also dedicated the sixth day, which after her name we call Friday."

Vortigern replied, "For your credulity, or rather incredulity, I am much grieved, but I rejoice at your arrival, which, whether by God's providence or some other agency, happens very seasonably for me in my present difficulties. For I am oppressed by my enemies on every side, and if you will engage with me in my wars, I will entertain you honourably in my kingdom, and bestow upon you lands and possessions." The barbarians readily accepted his offer, and the agreement between them being ratified, they resided at his court.

Soon after this, the Picts, issuing forth from Albania, with a very great army, began to lay waste the northern parts of the island. When Vortigern had information of it, he assembled his forces, and went to meet them beyond the Humber. Upon their engaging, the battle proved very fierce on both sides, though there was but little occasion for the Britons to exert themselves, for the Saxons fought so bravely, that the enemy, formerly so victorious, were speedily put to flight.

Vortigern, therefore, as he owed the victory to them, increased his bounty to them, and gave their general, Hengist, large possessions of land in Lindesia, for the subsistence of himself and his fellow soldiers. Hereupon Hengist, who was a man of experience and subtlety, finding how much interest he had with the king, addressed him in this manner:

"Sir, your enemies give you disturbance from all quarters, and few of your subjects love you. They all threaten you, and say they are going to bring over Aurelius Ambrosius from Armorica, to depose you, and make him king. If you please, let us send to our country to invite over some more soldiers, that with our forces increased we may be better able to oppose them. But there is one thing which I would desire of your clemency if I did not fear a refusal."

Vortigern made answer, "Send your messengers to Germany, and invite over whom you please, and you shall have no refusal from me in whatever you shall desire."

Hengist, with a low bow, returned him thanks, and said, "Give your servant," said Hengist, "only so much ground in the place you have assigned me, as I can encompass with a leathern thong, for me to build a fortress upon, as a place of retreat if occasion should require. For I will always be faithful to you, as I have been hitherto, and pursue no other design in the request which I have made."

With these words the king was prevailed upon to grant him his petition; and ordered him to despatch messengers to Germany, to invite more men over speedily to his assistance. Hengist immediately executed his orders, and taking a bull's hide, made one thong out of the whole, with which he encompassed a rocky place that had been carefully made choice of, and within that circuit began to build a castle; afterwards called, in the British tongue, Kaercorrei; in Saxon, Thancastre, that is, Thong Castle.

In the meantime, the messengers returned from Germany, with eighteen ships full of the best soldiers they could get. They also brought along with them Rowen, the daughter of Hengist, one of the most accomplished beauties of that age. After their arrival, Hengist invited the king to his house, to view his new buildings, and the new soldiers that were come over. The king readily accepted of his invitation, but privately, and having highly commended the magnificence of the structure, enlisted the men into his service.

Vortigern Marries

Here he was entertained at a royal banquet; and when that was over, the young lady came out of her chamber bearing a golden cup full of wine, with which she approached the king, and making a low courtesy, said to him, "Lauerd king wacht heil!" The king, at the sight of the lady's face, was on a sudden both surprised and inflamed with her beauty; and calling to his interpreter, asked him what she said, and what answer he should make her. "She called you Lord King," said the interpreter, "and offered to drink your health. Your answer must be, Drinc heil!" Vortigern accordingly answered, "Drinc heil" and bade her drink; after which he took the cup from her hand, kissed her, and drank himself. From that time to this, it has been the custom in Britain, that he who drinks to any one says, Wacht heil!, and he that pledges him answers Drinc heil!

Vortigern being now drunk with the variety of liquors, the devil took this opportunity to enter into his heart, and make him in love with the damsel, so that he became suitor to her father for her. It was, I say, by the devil's entering into his heart, that he, who was a Christian, should fall in love with a pagan.

By this example, Hengist, being a prudent man, discovered the king's levity, and consulted with his brother Horsa, and the other ancient men present, what to do in relation to the king's request. They unanimously advised him to give him his daughter, and in consideration of her to demand the province of Kent. Accordingly the daughter was without delay delivered to Vortigern, and the province of Kent to Hengist, without the knowledge of Gorangon, who had the government of it.

The king the same night married the pagan lady, and became extremely delighted with her; by which he quickly brought upon himself the hatred of the nobility, and of his own sons. For he had already three sons, whose names were Vortimer, Catigern, and Pascentius.

The king being now, as we have said, possessed of the lady, Hengist said to him: "As I am your father, I claim the right of being your counselor: do not therefore slight my advice, since it is to my countrymen you must owe the conquest of all your enemies. Let us invite over my son Octa and his brother Ebissa, who are brave soldiers, and give them the countries that are in the northern parts of Britain, by the wall, between Deira and Albania. For they will hinder the inroads of the barbarians, and so you shall enjoy peace on the other side of the Humber."

Vortigern complied with this request, and ordered them to invite over whomsoever they knew able to assist him. Immediately upon the receipt of this message, came Octa, Ebissa, and Cherdich, with three hundred ships filled with soldiers, who were all kindly received by Vortigern, and had ample presents made them. For by their assistance he vanquished his enemies, and in every engagement proved victorious.

Vortimer Battles the Saxons

Hengist in the meantime continued to invite over more and more ships, and to augment his numbers daily. Which when the Britons observed, they were afraid of being betrayed by them, and moved the king to banish them out of his coasts. For it was contrary to the rule of the gospel that Christians should hold fellowship, or have any intercourse, with pagans. Besides which, the number of those that were come over was now so great, that they were a terror to his subjects; and nobody could now know who was a pagan, and who a Christian, since pagans married the daughters and kinswomen of Christians. These things they represented to the king, and endeavoured to dissuade him from entertaining them, lest they might, by some treacherous conspiracy, prove an overmatch for the native inhabitants. But Vortigern, who loved them above all other nations on account of his wife, was deaf to their advice.

For this reason the Britons quickly desert him, and unanimously set up Vortimer his son for their king; who at their instigation began to drive out the barbarians, and to make dreadful incursions upon them. Four battles he fought with them, and was victorious in all: And when they were no longer able to bear the assaults of the Britons, they sent king Vortigern, who was present with them in all those wars, to his son Vortimer, to desire leave to depart, and return back safe to Germany. And while a conference upon this subject was being held, they in the meantime went on board their long galleys, and, leaving their wives and children behind them, returned back to Germany.

Vortimer, after this great success, began to restore his subjects to their possessions which had been taken from them, and to show them all marks of his affection and esteem, and at the instance of St. Germanus to rebuild their churches.

But his goodness quickly stirred up the enmity of the devil against him, who entering into the heart of his stepmother Rowen, excited her to contrive his death. For this purpose she consulted with the poisoners, and procured one who was intimate with him, whom she corrupted with large and numerous presents, to give him a poisonous draught; so that this brave soldier, as soon as he had taken it, was seized with a sudden illness, that deprived him of all hopes of life.

Hereupon he forthwith ordered all his men to come to him, and having shown them how near he was to his end, distributed among them all the treasure his predecessors had heaped up, and endeavoured to comfort them in their sorrow and lamentation for him, telling them, he was only going the way of all flesh. But he exhorted those brave and warlike young men, who had attended him in all his victories, to persist courageously in the defence of their country against all hostile invasion; and with wonderful greatness of mind, commanded a brazen pyramid to be placed in the port where the Saxons used to land, and his body when dead to be placed on the top of it, that the sight of his tomb might frighten back the barbarians to Germany. For he said none of them would dare approach the country, that should but get a sight of his tomb.

Such was the admirable bravery of this great man, who, as he had been a terror to them while living, endeavoured to be no less so when dead. Notwithstanding which, he was no sooner dead, than the Britons had no regard to his orders, and buried him at London.

The Saxons Return

Vortigern, after the death of his son, was again restored to the kingdom, and at the request of his wife sent messengers into Germany to Hengist, with an invitation to return into Britain, but privately, and with a small retinue, to prevent a quarrel between the barbarians and his subjects. But Hengist, hearing that Vortimer was dead, raised an army of not less than three hundred thousand men, and fitting out a fleet returned with them to Britain.

When Vortigern and the nobility heard of the arrival of so vast a multitude, they were immoderately incensed, and, after consultation together, resolved to fight them, and drive them from their coasts. Hengist, being informed of their design by messengers sent by his daughter, immediately entered into deliberation what course to pursue against them. After several stratagems had been considered, he judged it most feasible, to impose upon the nation by making show of peace.

With this view he sent ambassadors to the king, to declare to him, that he had not brought so great a number of men for the purpose either of staying with him, or offering any violence to the country. But the reason why he brought them, was because he thought Vortimer was yet living, and that he should have occasion for them against him, in case of an assault. But now since he no longer doubted of his being dead, he submitted himself and his people to the disposal of Vortigern; so that he might retain as many of them as he should think fit, and whomsoever he rejected Hengist would allow to return back without delay to Germany. And if these terms pleased Vortigern, he desired him to appoint a time and place for their meeting, and adjusting matters according to his pleasure.

When these things were represented to the king, he was mightily pleased, as being very unwilling to part with Hengist; and at last ordered his subjects and the Saxons to meet upon the kalends of May, which were now very near, at the monastery of Ambrius, for the settling of the matters above mentioned. The appointment being agreed to on both sides, Hengist, with a new design of villainy in his head, ordered his soldiers to carry every one of them a long dagger under their garments, and while the conference should be held with the Britons, who would have no suspicion of them, he would give this word of command, "Nemet oure Saxas"; at which moment they were all to be ready to seize boldly every one his next man, and with his drawn dagger stab him.

Accordingly they all met at the time and place appointed, and began to treat of peace; and when a fit opportunity offered for executing his villainy, Hengist cried out, "Nemet oure Saxas," and the same instant seized Vortigern, and held him by his cloak. The Saxons, upon the signal given, drew their daggers, and falling upon the princes, who little suspected any such design, assassinated them to the number of four hundred and sixty barons and consuls; to whose bodies St. Eldad afterwards gave Christian burial, not far from Kaercaradauc, now Salisbury, in a burying-place near the monastery of Ambrius, the abbot, who was the founder of it. For they all came without arms, having no thoughts of anything but treating of peace; which gave the others a fairer opportunity of exercising their villainous design against them.

But the pagans did not escape unpunished while they acted this wickedness; a great number of them being killed during this massacre of their enemies. For the Britons, taking up clubs and stones from the ground, resolutely defended themselves, and did good execution upon the traitors.

There was present one Eldol, consul of Gloucester, who, at the sight of this treachery, took up a stake which he happened to find, and with that made his defence. Every blow he gave carried death along with it; and by breaking either the head, arms, shoulders or legs of a great many, he struck no small terror into the traitors, nor did he move from the spot before he had killed with that weapon seventy men. But being no longer able to stand his ground against such numbers, he made his escape from them, and retired to his own city.

Many fell on both sides but the Saxons got the victory; because the Britons, having no suspicion of treachery, came unarmed, and therefore made a weaker defence.

After the commission of this detestable villainy, the Saxons would not kill Vortigern; but having threatened him with death and bound him, demanded his cities and fortified places in consideration of their granting him his life. He, to secure himself, denied them nothing; and when they had made him confirm his grants with an oath, they released him from his chains, and then marched first to London, which they took, as they did afterwards York, Lincoln, and Winchester; wasting the countries through which they passed, and destroying the people, as wolves do sheep when left by their shepherds.

The Youth Merlin

When Vortigern saw the desolation which they made, he retired into the parts of Cambria, not knowing what to do against so barbarous a people.

At last he had recourse to magicians for their advice, and commanded them to tell him what course to take. They advised him to build a very strong tower for his own safety, since he had lost all his other fortified places. Accordingly he made a progress about the country, to find out a convenient situation, and came at last to Mount Erir, where he assembled workmen from several countries, and ordered them to build the tower. The builders, therefore, began to lay the foundation; but whatever they did one day the earth swallowed up the next, so as to leave no appearance of their work.

Vortigern being informed of this again consulted with his magicians concerning the cause of it, who told him that he must find a youth that never had a father, and kill him, and then sprinkle the stones and cement with his blood; for by those means, they said, he would have a firm foundation.

Hereupon messengers were despatched away over all the provinces, to inquire out such a man. In their travels they came to a city, called afterwards Kaermerdin, where they saw some young men, playing before the gate, and went up to them; but being weary with their journey, they sat down in the ring, to see if they could meet with what they were in quest of. Towards evening, there happened on a sudden a quarrel between two of the young men, whose names were Merlin and Dabutius. In the dispute Dabutius said to Merlin, "You fool, do you presume to quarrel with me? Is there any equality in our birth? I am descended from a royal race, both by my father and mother's side. As for you, nobody knows what you are, for you never had a father."

At that word the messengers looked earnestly upon Merlin, and asked the bystanders who he was. They told him, it was not known who was his father; but that his mother was daughter to the king of Dimetia, and that she lived in St. Peter's church among the nuns of that city.

Upon this the messengers hastened to the governor of the city, and ordered him, in the king's name, to send Merlin and his mother to the king. As soon as the governor understood the occasion of their message, he readily obeyed the order, and sent them to Vortigern to complete his design. When they were introduced into the king's presence, he received the mother in a very respectful manner, on account of her noble birth; and began to inquire of her by what man she had conceived.

"My sovereign lord," said she, "by the life of your soul and mine, I know nobody that begot him of me. Only this I know, that as I was once with my companions in our chambers, there appeared to me a person in the shape of a beautiful young man, who often embraced me eagerly in his arms, and kissed me; and when he had stayed a little time, he suddenly vanished out of my sight. But many times after this he would talk with me when I sat alone, without making any visible appearance. When he had a long time haunted me in this manner, he at last laid with me several times in the shape of a man, and left me with child. And I do affirm to you, my sovereign lord, that excepting that young man, I know no body that begot him of me."

The king ordered Maugantius to be called, that he might satisfy him as to the possibility of what the woman had related. Maugantius, being introduced, and having the whole matter repeated to him, said to Vortigern: "In the books of our philosophers, and in a great many histories, I have found that several men have had the like original. For, as Apuleius informs us in his book concerning the Demon of Socrates, between the moon and the earth inhabit those spirits, which we will call incubuses. These are of the nature partly of men, and partly of angels, and whenever they please assume human shapes, and lie with women. Perhaps one of them appeared to this woman, and begot that young man of her."

Vortigern's Tower

Merlin in the meantime was attentive to all that had passed, and then approached the king, and said to him, "For what reason am I and my mother introduced into your presence?"

"My magicians," answered Vortigern, "advised me to seek out a man that had no father, with whose blood my building is to be sprinkled, in order to make it stand."

"Order your magicians," said Merlin, "to come before me, and I will convict them of a lie."

The king was surprised at his words, and presently ordered the magicians to come, and sit down before Merlin, who spoke to them after this manner: "Because you are ignorant what it is that hinders the foundation of the tower, you have recommended the shedding of my blood for cement to it, as if that would presently make it stand. But tell me now, what is there under the foundation? For something there is that will not suffer it to stand."

The magicians at this began to be afraid, and made no answer. Then said Merlin, who was also called Ambrose, "I entreat your majesty would command your workmen to dig into the ground, and you will find a pond which causes the foundation to sink." This accordingly was done, and then presently they found a pond deep under ground, which had made it give way.

Merlin after this went again to the magicians, and said, "Tell me ye false sycophants, what is there under the pond?" But they were silent. Then again he said to the king, "Command the pond to be drained, and at the bottom you will see two hollow stones, and in them two dragons asleep."

The king made no scruple of believing him, since he had found true what he said of the pond, and therefore ordered it to be drained: which done, he found as Merlin had said; and now was possessed with the greatest admiration of him. Nor were the rest that were present less amazed at his wisdom, thinking it to be no less than divine inspiration.

Chapter 2: The Prophesy of Merlin

Geoffrey's Introduction

I had not got thus far in my history, when the subject of public discourse happening to be concerning Merlin, I was obliged to publish his prophesies at the request of my acquaintances, but especially of Alexander, bishop of Lincoln, a prelate of the greatest piety and wisdom. Out of a desire to gratify him, I translated these prophecies, and sent them to him with the following letter.

"The regard which I owe to your great worth, most noble prelate, has obliged me to undertake the translation of Merlin's prophecies out of British into Latin, before I had made an end to the history which I had begun concerning the acts of the British kings. Since the deference which is paid to your penetrating judgment will screen me from censure, I have employed my rude pen, and in a coarse style present you with a translation out of a language with which you are unacquainted. Since it was your pleasure that Geoffrey of Monmouth should be employed in this prophesy, he hopes that you will favourably accept of his performance, and vouchsafe to give a finer turn to whatever you shall find unpolished, or otherwise faulty in it."

As Vortigern, king of the Britons, was sitting upon the bank of the drained pond, the two dragons, one of which was white, the other red, came forth, and, approaching one another, began a terrible fight, and cast forth fire with their breath. But the white dragon had the advantage, and made the other fly to the end of the lake. And he, for grief at his flight, renewed the assault upon his pursuer, and forced him to retire. After this battle of the dragons, the king commanded Ambrose Merlin to tell him what it portended. Upon which he, bursting into tears, delivered what his prophetical spirit suggested to him, as follows: —

The Near Future

"Woe to the red dragon, for his banishment hasteneth on. His lurking holes shall be seized by the white dragon, which signifies the Saxons whom you invited over; but the red denotes the British nation, which shall be oppressed by the white. Therefore shall its mountains be levelled as the valleys, and the rivers of the valleys shall run with blood. The exercise of religion shall be destroyed, and churches laid open to ruin.

At last the oppressed shall prevail, and oppose the

cruelty of foreigners. For a boar of Cornwall[3] shall give his assistance, and trample their necks under his feet. The islands of the ocean shall be subject to his power, and he shall possess the forests of Gaul. The house of Romulus shall dread his courage, and his end shall be doubtful. He shall be celebrated in the mouths of the people; and his exploits shall be food to those that relate them.

Six of his posterity shall sway the sceptre, but after them shall arise a German worm. He shall be advanced by a sea-wolf, whom the woods of Africa shall accompany. Religion shall again be abolished, and there shall be a translation of the metropolitan sees. The dignity of London shall adorn Dorobernia, and the seventh pastor of York shall be resorted to in the kingdom of Armorica. St David's shall put on the pall of the City of Legions, and a preacher of Ireland shall be dumb on account of an infant growing in the womb. It shall rain a shower of blood, and a raging famine shall afflict mankind.

The Saxons Conquer Britain

When these things happen, the red one shall be grieved; but when his fatigue is over, shall grow strong. Then shall misfortunes hasten upon the white one, and the buildings of his gardens shall be pulled down. Seven that sway the

---

[3] The boar of Cornwall is Arthur. This section prophesies events that are described in the chapters about Arthur and in the later chapters of Geoffrey's *History*. The following sections are prophesies about the more distant future.

sceptre shall be killed, one of whom shall become a saint. The wombs of mothers shall be ripped up, and infants be abortive. There shall be a most grievous punishment of men, that the natives may be restored. He that shall do these things shall put on the brazen man, and upon a brazen horse shall for a long time guard the gates of London.

After this, shall the red dragon return to his proper manners, and turn his rage upon himself. Therefore shall the revenge of the Thunderer show itself, for every field shall disappoint the husbandmen. Mortality shall snatch away the people, and make a desolation over all countries. The remainder shall quit their native soil, and make foreign plantations. A blessed king shall prepare a fleet, and shall be reckoned the twelfth in the court among the saints. There shall be a miserable desolation of the kingdom, and the floors of the harvests shall return to the fruitful forests.

The white dragon shall rise again, and invite over a daughter of Germany. Our gardens shall be again replenished with foreign seed, and the red one shall pine away at the end of the pond.

After that shall the German worm be crowned, and the brazen prince buried. He has his bounds assigned him, which he shall not be able to pass. For a hundred and fifty years he shall continue in trouble and subjection, but shall bear sway three hundred. Then shall the north wind rise against him, and shall snatch away the flowers which the west wind produced. There shall be gilding in the temples, nor shall the edge of the sword cease. The German dragon shall hardly get to his holes, because the revenge of his treason shall overtake him.

The Britons Defeat the Normans

At last he shall flourish for a little time, but the decimation of Neustria[4] shall hurt him. For a people in wood and in iron coats shall come, and revenge on him his wickedness. They shall restore the ancient inhabitants to their dwellings, and there shall be an open destruction of foreigners. The seed of the while dragon shall be swept out of our gardens, and the remainder of his generation shall be decimated. They shall bear the yoke of slavery, and wound their mother with spades and ploughs.

After this shall succeed two dragons, whereof one shall be killed with the sting of envy, but the other shall return under the shadow of a name.

Then shall succeed a lion of justice, at whose roar the Gallican towers and the island dragons shall tremble. In those days gold shall be squeezed from the lily and the nettle, and silver shall flow from the hoofs of bellowing cattle. The frizzled shall put on various fleeces, and the outward habit denote the inward parts. The feet of barkers shall be cut off; wild beasts shall enjoy peace; mankind shall be grieved at their punishment; the form of commerce shall be divided; the half shall be round. The ravenousness of kites shall be destroyed, and the teeth of wolves blunted. The lion's whelps shall be transformed into sea-fishes; and

[4] The French Province of Normandy.

an eagle shall build her nest upon Mount Aravius. Venedotia shall grow red with the blood of mothers, and the house of Corineus kill six brethren. The island shall be wet with night tears; so that all shall be provoked to all things.

Woe to thee, Neustria, because the lion's brain shall be poured upon thee: and he shall be banished with shattered limbs from his native soil. Posterity shall endeavour to fly above the highest places; but the favour of new comers shall be exalted. Piety shall hurt the possessor of things got by impiety, till he shall have put on his Father; therefore, being armed with the teeth of a boar, he shall ascend above the tops of the mountains, and the shadow of him that wears a helmet.

Albania shall be enraged, and, assembling her neighbours, shall be employed in shedding blood. There shall be put into her jaws a bridle that shall be made on the coast of Armorica. The eagle of the broken covenant shall gild it over, and rejoice in her third nest. The roaring whelps shall watch, and, leaving the woods, shall hunt within the walls of cities. They shall make no small slaughter of those that oppose them, and shall cut off the tongues of bulls. They shall load the necks of roaring lions with chains, and restore the times of their ancestors. Then from the first to the fourth, from the fourth to the third, from the third to the second, the thumb shall roll in oil.

The sixth shall overturn the walls of Ireland, and change the woods into a plain. He shall reduce several parts to one, and be crowned with the head of a lion. His beginning shall lay open to wandering affection, but his end shall carry him up to the blessed, who are above. For he shall restore the seats of saints in their countries, and settle pastors in convenient places. Two cities he shall invest with two palls, and shall bestow virgin-presents upon virgins. He shall merit by this the favour of the Thunderer, and shall be placed among the saints.

From him shall proceed a lynx penetrating all things, who shall be bent upon the ruin of his own nation; for, through him, Neustria shall lose both islands, and be deprived of its ancient dignity. Then shall the natives return back to the island; for there shall arise a dissention among foreigners. Also a hoary old man, sitting upon a snow-white horse, shall turn the course of the river Periron, and shall measure out a mill upon it with a white rod.

They shall break forth the fountains of Armorica, and they shall be crowned with the diadem of Brutus. Cambria shall be filled with joy; and the oaks of Cornwall shall flourish. The island shall be called by the name of Brutus:[5] and the name given it by foreigners shall be abolished.

From Conan shall proceed a warlike boar, that shall exercise the sharpness of his tusks within the Gallic woods. For he shall cut down all the larger oaks, and shall be a defence to the smaller. The Arabians and Africans shall dread him; for he shall pursue a furious course to the farther part of Spain.

[5] Brutus, who fled from Troy with Aeneas, is the mythical founder of Britain in Geoffrey's *History*. Geoffrey believed that Britain was named after Brutus.

Evil Kings of Britain

There shall succeed the goat of the Venereal castle, having golden horns and a silver beard, who shall breathe such a cloud out of his nostrils, as shall darken the whole surface of the island. There shall be peace in his time; and corn shall abound by reason of the fruitfulness of the soil. Women shall become serpents in their gait, and all their motions shall be full of pride. The camp of Venus shall be restored; nor shall the arrows of Cupid cease to wound. The fountain of a river shall be turned into blood; and two kings shall fight a duel at Stafford for a lioness. Luxury shall overspread the whole ground; and fornication not cease to debauch mankind.

All these things shall three ages see; till the buried kings shall be exposed to public view in the city of London. Famine shall again return; and the inhabitants shall grieve for the destruction of their cities. Then shall come the board of commerce, who shall recall the scattered flocks to the pasture they had lost. His breast shall be food to the hungry, and his tongue drink to the thirsty. Out of his mouth shall flow rivers, that shall water the parched jaws of men.

After this shall be produced a tree upon the Tower of London, which, having no more than three branches, shall overshadow the surface of the whole island with the breadth of its leaves. Its adversary, the north wind, shall come upon it, and with its noxious blast shall snatch away the third branch, but the two remaining ones shall possess its place, till they shall destroy one another by the multitude of their leaves; and then shall it obtain the place of those two, and shall give sustenance to birds of foreign nations. It shall be esteemed hurtful to native fowls; for they shall not be able to fly freely for fear of its shadow.

There shall succeed the ass of wickedness, swift against the goldsmiths, but slow against the ravenousness of wolves. In those days the oaks of the forests shall burn, and acorns grow upon the branches of tell trees. The Severn sea shall discharge itself through seven mouths, and the river Uske burn seven months. Fishes shall die with the heat thereof; and of them shall be engendered serpents. The baths of Badon shall grow cold, and their salubrious waters engender death. London shall mourn for the death of twenty thousand; and the river Thames shall be turned to blood. The monks in their cowls shall be forced to marry, and their cry shall be heard upon the mountains of the Alps.

Britain Divided in Three

Three springs shall break forth in the city of Winchester, whose rivulets shall divide the island into three parts, Whoever shall drink of the first, shall enjoy long life, and shall never be afflicted with sickness. He that shall drink of the second, shall die of hunger, and paleness and horror shall sit in his countenance. He that shall drink of the third, shall be surprised with sudden death, neither shall his body be capable of burial.

Those that are willing to escape so great a surfeit, will endeavour to hide it with several coverings: but whatever bulk shall be laid upon it, shall receive the form of another body. For earth shall be turned into stones; stones into water; wood into ashes; ashes into water, if cast over it.

Also a damsel shall be sent from the city of the forest of Cantune to administer a cure, who, after she shall have practiced all her arts, shall dry up the noxious fountains herself with the wholesome liquor, she shall bear in her right hand the wood of Caledon, and in her left the forts of the walls of London. Wherever she shall go, she shall make sulphurous steps, which will smoke with a double flame.

That smoke shall rouse up the city of the Ruteni, and shall make food for the inhabitants of the deep. She shall overflow with rueful tears, and shall fill the island with her dreadful cry. She shall be killed by a hart with ten branches, four of which shall bear golden diadems; but the other six shall be turned into buffalo's horns, whose hideous sounds shall astonish the three islands of Britain.

The Daneian wood shall be stirred up, and breaking forth into a human voice, shall cry: Come, O Cambria, and join Cornwall to thy side, and say to Winchester, the earth shall swallow thee up. Translate the seat of thy pastor to the place where ships come to harbour, and the rest of the members will follow the head. For the day hasteneth, in which thy citizens shall perish on account of the guilt of perjury. The whiteness of wool has been hurtful to thee, and the variety of its tinctures. Woe to the perjured nation, for whose sake the renowned city shall come to ruin. The ships shall rejoice at so great an augmentation, and one shall be made out of two.

It shall be rebuilt by Eric, loaden with apples, to the smell whereof the birds of several woods shall flock together. He shall add to it a vast palace, and wall it round with six hundred towers. Therefore shall London envy it, and triply increase her walls. The river Thames shall encompass it round, and the fame of the work shall pass beyond the Alps. Eric shall hide his apples within it, and shall make subterraneous passages.

At that time shall the stones speak, and the sea towards the Gallic coast be contracted into a narrow space. On each bank shall one man hear another, and the soil of the island shall be enlarged. The secrets of the deep shall be revealed, and Gaul shall tremble for fear.

After these things shall come forth a heron from the forest of Calaterium, which shall fly round the island for two years together. With her nocturnal cry she shall call together with winged kind, and assemble to her all sorts of fowls. They shall invade the tillage of a husbandman, and devour all the grain of the harvests. Then shall follow a famine upon the people, and a grievous mortality upon the famine.

Fox, Wolf and Bear

But when this calamity shall be over, a detestable bird shall go to the valley of Galabes, and shall raise it to be a high mountain. Upon the top thereof it shall also plant an oak, and build its nest in its branches. Three eggs shall be produced in the nest, from whence shall come forth a fox, a wolf, and a bear.

The fox shall devour her mother, and bear the head of an ass. In this monstrous form shall she frighten her brothers, and make them fly into Neustria. But they shall stir up the tusky boar, and returning in a fleet shall encounter with the fox; who at the beginning of the fight shall feign herself dead, and move the boar to compassion. Then shall the boar approach her carcass, and standing over her, shall breathe upon her face and eyes. But she, not forgetting her cunning, shall bite his left foot, and pluck it off from his boy. Then shall she leap upon him, and snatch away his right ear and tail, and hide herself in the caverns of the mountains.

Therefore shall the deluded boar require the wolf and bear to restore him his members; who, as soon as they shall enter into the cause, shall promise two feet of the fox, together with the ear and tail, and of these they shall make up the members of a hog. With this he shall be satisfied, and expect the promised restitution.

In the meantime shall the fox descend from the mountains, and change herself into a wolf, and under pretense of holding a conference with the boar, she shall go to him, and craftily devour him. After that she shall transform herself into a boar, and feigning a loss of some members, shall wait for her brothers; but as soon as they are come, she shall suddenly kill them with her tusks, and shall be crowned with the head of a lion.

In her days shall a serpent be brought forth, which shall be a devourer of mankind. With its length it shall encompass London, and devour all that pass by it. The mountain ox shall take the head of a wolf, and whiten his teeth in the Severn. He shall gather to him the flocks of Albania and Cambria, which shall drink the river Thames dry. The ass shall call the goat with the long beard, and shall borrow his shape. Therefore shall the mountain ox be incensed, and having called the wolf, shall become a horned bull against them. In the exercise of his cruelty he shall devour their flesh and bones, but shall be buried upon the top of Urian.

The ashes of his funeral-pile shall be turned into swans, that shall swim on dry ground as on a river. They shall devour fishes in fishes, and swallow up men in men. But when old age shall come upon them, they shall become sea-wolves, and practice their frauds in the deep. They shall drown ships, and collect no small quantity of silver.

The Thames shall again flow, and assembling together the rivers, shall pass beyond the bounds of its channel. It shall cover the adjacent cities, and overturn the mountains that oppose its course. Being full of deceit and wickedness, it shall make use of the fountain Galabes. Hence shall arise factions provoking the Venedotians to war. The oaks of the forest shall meet together, and encounter the rocks of the Gewisseans. A raven shall attend with the kites, and devour the carcasses of the slain.

An owl shall build her nest upon the walls of Gloucester, and in her nest shall be brought forth an ass. The serpent of Malvernia shall bring him up, and put him upon many fraudulent practices. Having taken the crown, he shall ascend on high, and frighten the people of the country with his hideous braying.

Evil Rulers

In his days shall the Pachaian mountains tremble, and the provinces be deprived of their woods. For there shall come a worm with a fiery breath, and with the vapour it sends forth shall burn up the trees. Out of it shall proceed seven lions deformed with the heads of goats. With the stench of their nostrils they shall corrupt women, and make wives turn common prostitutes. The father shall not know his own son, because they shall grow wanton like brute beasts.

Then shall come the giant of wickedness, and terrify all with the sharpness of his eyes. Against him shall arise the dragon of Worcester, and shall endeavour to banish him. But in the engagement the dragon shall be worsted, and oppressed by the wickedness of the conqueror. For he shall mount upon the dragon, and putting off his garment shall sit upon him naked. The dragon shall bear him up on high, and beat his naked rider with his tail erected. Upon this the giant rousing up his whole strength, shall break his jaws with his sword. At last the dragon shall fold itself up under its tail, and die of poison.

After him shall succeed the boar of Totness, and oppress the people with grievous tyranny. Gloucester shall send forth a lion, and shall disturb him in his cruelty, in several battles. He shall trample him under his feet, and terrify him with open jaws.

At last the lion shall quarrel with the kingdom, and get upon the backs of the nobility. A bull shall come into the quarrel, and strike the lion with his right foot. He shall drive him through all the inns in the kingdom, but shall break his horns against the walls of Oxford.

The fox of Kaerdubalem shall take revenge on the lion, and destroy him entirely with her teeth. She shall be encompassed by the adder of Lincoln who with a horrible hiss shall give notice of his presence to a multitude of dragons. Then shall the dragons encounter, and tear one another to pieces. The winged shall oppress that which wants wings and fasten its claws into the poisonous cheeks. Others shall come into the quarrel, and kill one another.

A fifth shall succeed those that are slain, and by various stratagems shall destroy the rest. He shall get upon the back of one with his sword, and sever his head from his body. Then throwing off his garment, he shall get upon another, and put his rights and left hand upon his tail. Thus being naked shall he overcome him, whom when clothed he was not able to deal with. The rest he shall gall in their flight, and drive them round the kingdom.

Upon this shall come a roaring lion dreadful for his monstrous cruelty. Fifteen parts shall he reduce to one, and shall alone possess the people. The giants of the now-white colour shall shine, and cause the white people to flourish. Pleasures shall eliminate the princes, and they shall suddenly be changed into beasts. Among them shall arise a lion swelled with human gore. Under him shall a reaper be placed in the standing corn, who, while he is reaping, shall be oppressed by him.

A charioteer of York shall appease them, and having banished his lord, shall mount upon the chariot which he shall drive. With his sword unsheathed shall he threaten the East, and fill the tracks of his wheels with blood. Afterwards he shall become a sea-fish, who, being roused up with the hissing of a serpent, shall engender with him. From hence shall be produced three thundering bulls, who having eaten up their pastures shall be turned into trees. The first shall carry a whip of vipers, and turn his back upon the next. He shall endeavour to snatch away the whip, but shall be taken by the last. They shall turn away their faces from one another, till they have thrown away the poisoned cup.

To him shall succeed a husbandman of Albania, at whose back shall be a serpent. He shall be employed in ploughing the ground, that the country may become white with corn. The serpent shall endeavour to diffuse his poison, in order to blast the harvest. A grievous mortality shall sweep away the people, and the walls of cities shall be made desolate.

Dust of the Ancients Restored

There shall be given for a remedy the city of Claudius, which shall interpose the nurse of the scourger. For he shall bear a dose of medicine, and in a short time the island shall be restored.

Then shall two successively sway the sceptre, whom a horned dragon shall serve. One shall come in armour, and shall ride upon a flying serpent. He shall sit upon his back with his naked body, and cast his right hand upon his tail. With his cry shall the seas be moved, and he shall strike terror into the second.

The second therefore shall enter into confederacy with the lion; but a quarrel happening, they shall encounter one another. They shall distress one another, but the courage of the beast shall gain the advantage. Then shall come one with a drum, and appease the rage of the lion.

Therefore shall the people of the kingdom be at peace,

and provoke the lion to a dose of physic. In his established seat he shall adjust the weights, but shall stretch out his hands into Albania. For which reason the northern provinces shall be grieved, and open the gates of the temples.

The sign-bearing wolf shall lead his troops, and surround Cornwall with his tail. He shall be opposed by a soldier in a chariot, who shall transform that people into a boar. The boar therefore shall ravage the provinces, but shall hide his head in the depth of the Severn. A man shall embrace a lion in wine, and the dazzling brightness of gold shall blind the eyes of beholders. Silver shall whiten in the circumference, and torment several wine presses.

Men shall be drunk with wine, and, regardless of heaven, shall be intent upon the earth. From them shall the stars turn away their faces, and confound their usual course. Corn will wither at their malign aspects; and there shall fall no dew from heaven. The roots and branches will change their places, and the novelty of the thing shall pass for a miracle.

The brightness of the sun shall fade at the amber of Mercury, and horror shall seize the beholders. Silbon of Arcadia shall change his shield; the helmet of Mars shall call Venus. The helmet of Mars shall make a shadow; and the rage of Mercury pass his bounds. Iron Orion shall unsheathe his sword: the marine Phoebus shall torment the clouds; Jupiter shall go out of his lawful paths; and Venus forsake her stated lines. The malignity of the star Saturn shall fall down in rain, and slay mankind with a crooked sickle. The twelve houses of the star shall lament the irregular excursions of their guests; and Gemini omit their usual embraces, and call the urn to the fountains. The scales of Libra shall hand obliquely, till Aries puts his crooked horns under them. The tail of Scorpio shall produce lightning, and Cancer quarrel with the Sun. Virgo shall mount upon the back of Sagittarius, and darken her virgin flowers. The chariot of the moon shall disorder the zodiac, and the Pleiades break forth into weeping.

No offices of Janus shall hereafter return, but his gate being shut shall lie hid in the chinks of Ariadne. The seas shall rise up in the twinkling of an eye, and the dust of the ancients shall be restored. The winds shall fight together with a dreadful blast, and their sound shall reach the stars.

Chapter 3: King Aurelius Ambrosius

Vortigern's Fate

Merlin, by delivering these and many other prophesies, caused in all that were present an admiration at the ambiguity of his expressions. But Vortigern above all the rest both admired and applauded the wisdom and prophetical spirit of the young man: for that age had produced none that ever talked in such a manner before him.

Being therefore curious to learn his own fate, he desired the young man to tell him what he knew concerning that particular. Merlin answered: "Fly the fire of the sons of Constantine, if you are able to do it: already they are fitting out their ships; already are they leaving the Armorican shore; already are they spreading out their sails to the wind. They will steer towards Britain; they will invade the Saxon nation; they will subdue that wicked people; but they will first burn you being shut up in a tower. To your own ruin did you prove a traitor to their father, and invite the Saxons into the island. You invited them for your safeguard; but they came for a punishment to you.

"Two deaths instantly threaten you; nor is it easy to determine which you can best avoid. For on the one hand the Saxons shall lay waste your country, and endeavour to kill you; on the other shall arrive the two brothers, Aurelius Ambrosius and Uther Pendragon, whose business will be to revenge their father's murder on you. Seek out some refuge if you can: to-morrow they will be on the shore of Totness.

"The faces of the Saxons shall look red with blood, Hengist shall be killed, and Aurelius Ambrosius shall be crowned. He shall bring peace to the nation; he shall restore the churches; but shall die of poison. His brother Uther Pendragon shall succeed him, whose days also shall be cut short by poison. There shall be present at the commission of this treason your own issue, whom the boar of Cornwall shall devour."

Accordingly the next day early, arrived Aurelius Ambrosius and his brother, with ten thousand men.

The Death of Vortigern

As soon as news of his coming was divulged, the Britons, who had been dispersed by their great calamities, met together from all parts, and gaining this new accession of strength from their countrymen, displayed unusual vigour. Having assembled together the clergy, they anointed Aurelius king, and paid him the customary homage. And when the people were urgent to fall upon the Saxons, he dissuaded them from it, because his desire was to pursue Vortigern first. For the treason committed against his father so very much affected him, that he thought nothing done till that was first avenged. In pursuance therefore of his design, he marched with his army into Cambria, to the town of Genroreu, whither Vortigern had fled for refuge. That town was in the country of Hergin, upon the river Gania, in the mountains called Cloarius. As soon as Ambrosius was arrived there, bearing in mind the murder of his father and brother, he spake thus to Eldol, duke of Gloucester.

"See, most noble duke, whether the walls of this city are able to protect Vortigern against my sheathing this sword in his bowels. He deserves to die, and you cannot, I suppose, be ignorant of his desert. Oh most villainous of men, whose crimes deserve inexpressible tortures! First he betrayed my father Constantine, who had delivered him and his country from the inroads of the Picts; afterwards my brother Constans whom he made king on purpose to destroy him. Again, when by his craft he had usurped the crown, he introduced pagans among the natives, in order to abuse those who continued steadfast in their loyalty to me: but by the good providence of God, he unwarily fell into the snare which he had laid for my faithful subjects. For the Saxons, when they found him out in his wickedness, drove him from the kingdom; for which nobody ought to be concerned. But this I think matter of just grief, that this odious people, whom that detestable traitor invited over, has expelled the nobility, laid waste a fruitful country, destroyed the holy churches, and almost extinguished Christianity over the whole kingdom. Now, therefore, my countrymen, show yourselves men: first revenge yourselves upon him that was the occasion of all these disasters; then let us turn our arms against our enemies, and free our country from their brutish tyranny."

Immediately, therefore, they set their engines to work, and laboured to beat down the walls. But at last, when all other attempts failed, they had recourse to fire, which meeting with proper fuel, ceased not to rage, till it had burned down the tower and Vortigern in it.

The Death of Hengist

Hengist, with his Saxons, was struck with terror at this news, for he dreaded the valour of Aurelius. Such was the bravery and courage this prince was master of, that while he was in Gaul, there was none that durst encounter with him. For in all encounters he either dismounted his adversary, or broke his spear. Besides, he was magnificent in his presents, constant at his devotions, temperate in all respects, and above all things hated a lie. A brave soldier on foot, a better on horseback, and expert in the discipline of an army. Reports of these his noble accomplishments, while he yet continued in Armorican Britain, were daily brought over into the island.

Therefore the Saxons, in fear of him, retired beyond the Humber, and in those parts fortified the cities and towns; for that country always was a place of refuge to them; their safety lying in the neighbourhood of Scotland, which used to watch all opportunities of distressing the nation; for that country being in itself a frightful place to live in, and wholly uninhabited, had been a safe retreat for strangers. By its situation it lay open to the Picts, Scots, Dacians, Norwegians, and others, that came to plunder the island. Being, therefore, secure of a safe reception in this country, they fled towards it, that, if there should be occasion, they might retreat into it as into their own camp.

This was good news to Aurelius, and made him conceive greater hopes of victory. So assembling his people quickly together, he augmented his army, and made an expeditious march towards the north. In his passage through the countries, he was grieved to see the desolation made in them, but especially that the churches were levelled with the ground; and he promised to rebuild them, if he gained the victory.

But Hengist, upon his approach, took courage again, and chose out the bravest of his men, whom he exhorted to make a gallant defence, and not be daunted at Aurelius, who, he told them, had but few Armorican Britons with him, since their number did not exceed ten thousand. And as for the native Britons, he made no account of them, since they had been so often defeated by him. He therefore promised them the victory, and that they should come off safely, considering the superiority of their number, which amounted to two hundred thousand men in arms.

After he had in this manner animated his men, he advanced with them towards Aurelius, into a field called Maisbeli, through which Aurelius was to pass. For his intention was to make a sudden assault by a surprise, and fall upon the Britons before they were prepared. But Aurelius perceived the design, and yet did not, on that account, delay going to the field, but rather pursued his march with more expedition. When he was come within sight of the enemy, he put his troops in order, commanding three thousand Armoricans to attend the cavalry, and drew out the rest together with the islanders into line of battle. The Dimetians he placed upon the hills, and the Venedotians in the adjacent woods. His reason for which was, that they might be there ready to fall upon the Saxons, in case they should flee in that direction.

In the meantime, Eldol, duke of Gloucester, went to the king, and said, "This one day should suffice for all the days of my life, if by good providence I could but get an opportunity to engage with Hengist; for one of us should die before we parted. I still retain deeply fixed in my memory the day appointed for our peaceably treating together, but which he villainously made use of to assassinate all that were present at the treaty, except myself only, who stood upon my defence with a stake which I accidentally found, until I made my escape. That very day proved fatal, through his treachery, to no less than four hundred and sixty barons and consuls, who all went unarmed. From that conspiracy God was pleased to deliver me, by throwing a stake in my way, wherewith I defended myself and escaped."

Thus spoke Eldol. Then Aurelius exhorted his companions to place all their hope on the Son of God, and to make a brave assault with one consent upon the enemy, in defence of their country. Nor was Hengist less busy on the other hand in forming his troops, and giving them directions how to behave themselves in the battle; and he walked himself through their several ranks, the more to spirit themselves up. At last, both armies, being drawn out in order of battle, began the attack, which they maintained with great bravery, and no small loss of blood, both to the Britons and Saxons.

Aurelius animated the Christians, Hengist the pagans; and all the time of the engagement, Eldol's chief endeavour was to encounter Hengist, but he had no opportunity for it. For Hengist, when he found that his own men were routed, and that the Christians, by the especial favour of God, had the advantage, fled to the town called Kaerconan, now Cunungeburg. Aurelius pursued him, and either killed or made slaves of all he found in the way.

When Hengist saw that he was pursued by Aurelius, he would not enter the town, but assembled his troops, and prepared them to stand another engagement. For he knew the town would not hold out against Aurelius, and that his whole security now lay in his sword. At last Aurelius overtook him, and after marshalling his forces, began another most furious fight. And here the Saxons steadily maintained their ground, notwithstanding the numbers that fell. On both side there was a great slaughter, the groans of the dying causing a greater rage in those that survived.

In short, the Saxons would have gained the day, had not a detachment of horse from the Armorican Britons come in upon them. For Aurelius had appointed them the same station which they had in the former battle; so that, upon their advancing, the Saxons gave ground, and when once a little dispersed, were not able to rally again. The Britons, encouraged by this advantage, exerted themselves, and laboured with all their might to distress the enemy. All the time Aurelius was fully employed, not only in giving commands, but encouraging his men by his own example; for with his own hand he killed all that stood in his way, and pursued those that fled. Nor was Eldol less active in all parts of the field, running to and fro to assault his adversaries; but still his main endeavour was to find opportunity of encountering Hengist.

As there were therefore several movements made by the parties engaged on each side, an opportunity occurred for their meeting, and briskly engaging each other. In this encounter of the two greatest champions in the field, the fire sparked with the clashing of their arms, and every stroke in a manner produced both thunder and lightning. For a long time was the victory in suspense, as it seemed sometimes to favour one, sometimes the other. While they were thus hotly engaged, Gorlois, duke of Cornwall, came up to them with the party he commanded, and did great execution upon the enemies' troops. At the sight of him, Eldol, assured of victory, seized on the helmet of Hengist, and by main force dragged him in among the Britons, and then in transports of joy cried out with a loud voice, "God has fulfilled my desire! My brave soldiers, down, down, with your enemies the Ambrons. The victory is now in your hands: Hengist is defeated, and the day is your own."

In the meantime the Britons failed not to perform every one his part against the pagans, upon whom they made many vigorous assaults; and though they were obliged sometimes to give ground, yet their courage did not fail them in making a good resistance; so that they gave the enemy no respite till they had vanquished them. The Saxons therefore fled whithersoever their consternation hurried them, some to the cities, some to the woods upon the hills, and others to their ships. But Octa, the son of Hengist, made his retreat with a great body of men to York: and Eosa, his kinsman, to the city of Alclud, where he had a very large army for his guard.

Aurelius, after this victory, took the city of Conan above-mentioned, and stayed there three days. During this time he gave orders for the burial of the slain, for curing the wounded, and for the ease and refreshment of his forces that were fatigued.

Then he called a council of his principal officers, to deliberate what was to be done with Hengist. There was present at the assembly Eldad, bishop of Gloucester, and brother of Eldol, a prelate of very great wisdom and piety. As soon as he beheld Hengist standing in the king's presence, he demanded silence, and said, "Though all should be unanimous for setting him at liberty, yet would I cut him to pieces. The prophet Samuel is my warrant, who when he had Agag, king of Amalek, in his power, hewed him in pieces, saying, "As thy sword hath made women childless, so shall thy mother be childless among women. Do the same to Hengist, who is a second Agag." Accordingly Eldol took his sword, and drew him out of the city, and then cut off his head. But Aurelius, who showed moderation in all his conduct, commanded him to be buried and a heap of earth to be raised over his body, according to the custom of the pagans.

The Restoration of Britain

From hence Aurelius conducted his army to York, to besiege Octa, Hengist's son. When the city was invested, Octa was doubtful whether he should give any opposition, and stand a siege against such a powerful an army. After consultation upon it, he went out with his principal nobility that were present, carrying a chain in his hand, and sand upon his head, and presented himself to the king with this address: "My gods are vanquished, and I doubt not that the sovereign power is in your God, who has compelled so many noble persons to come before you in this suppliant manner. Be pleased therefore to accept of us, and of this chain. If you do not think us fit objects of your clemency, we here present ourselves ready to be fettered, and to undergo whatever punishment you shall adjudge to us."

Aurelius was moved with pity at the spectacle, and demanded the advice of his council what should be done with them. After various proposals upon this subject, Eldad the bishop rose up, and delivered his opinion in these words: "The Gibeonites came voluntarily to the children of Israel to desire mercy, and they obtained it. And shall we Christians be worse than the Jews, in refusing them mercy? It is mercy which they beg, and let them have it. The island of Britain is large, and in many places uninhabited. Let us make a covenant with them, and suffer them at least to inhabit the desert places, that they may be our vassals for ever."

The king acquiesced in Eldad's advice, and suffered them to partake of his clemency. After this Eosa and the rest that fled, being encouraged by Octa's success, came also, and were admitted to the same favour. The king therefore granted them the country bordering upon Scotland, and made a firm covenant with them.

The enemies being now entirely reduced, the king summoned the consuls and princes of the kingdom together at York, where he gave orders for the restoration of the churches, which the Saxons had destroyed. He himself undertook the rebuilding of the metropolitan church of that city, as also the other cathedral churches in that province. After fifteen days, when he had settled workmen in various places, he went to London, which city had not escaped the fury of the enemy. He beheld with great sorrow the destruction made in it, and recalled the remainder of the citizens from all parts, and began the restoration of it.

Here he settled the affairs of the whole kingdom, revived the laws, restored the right heirs to the possessions of their ancestors; and those estates, whereof the heirs had been lost in the late grievous calamity, he distributed among his fellow soldiers. In these important concerns, of restoring the nation to its ancient state, repairing the churches, re-establishing peace and law, and settling the administration of justice, was his time wholly employed.

From hence he went to Winchester, to repair the ruins of it, as he did of other cities; and when the work was finished there, he went, at the instance of bishop Eldad, to the monastery near Kaercaradoc, now Salisbury, where the consuls and princes, whom the wicked Hengist had treacherously murdered, lay buried. At this place was a convent that maintained three hundred friars, situated on the mountain of Ambrius, who, as is reported, had been the founder of it. The sight of the place where the dead lay made the king, who was of a compassionate temper, shed tears, and at last enter upon thoughts, what kind of monument to erect upon it. For he thought something ought to be done to perpetuate the memory of that piece of ground, which was honoured with the bodies of so many noble patriots, that died for their country.

For this purpose he summoned together several carpenters and masons, and commanded them to employ the utmost of their art, in contriving some new structure, for a lasting monument to those great men. But they, in diffidence of their own skill, refusing to undertake it, Tremounus, archbishop of the City of Legions, went to the king, and said, "If any one living is able to execute your commands, Merlin, the prophet of Vortigern, is the man. In my opinion there is not in all your kingdom a person of brighter genius, either in predicting future events, or in mechanical contrivances. Order him to come to you, and exercise his skill in the work which you design."

Merlin Builds Stonehenge

Whereupon Aurelius, after he had asked a great many questions concerning him, despatched several messengers into the country to find him out, and bring him to him. After passing through several provinces, they found him in the country of the Gewisseans, at the fountain of Galabes, which he frequently resorted to. As soon as they had delivered their message to him, they conducted him to the king, who received him with joy, and, being curious to hear some of his wonderful speeches, commanded him to prophesy.

Merlin made answer: "Mysteries of this kind are not to be revealed but when there is the greatest necessity for it. If I should pretend to utter them for ostentation or diversion, the spirit that instructs me would be silent, and would leave me when I should have occasion for it."

When he had made the same refusal to all the rest present, the king would not urge him any longer about his predictions, but spoke to him concerning the monument which he designed.

"If you are desirous," said Merlin, "to honour the burying-place of these men with an everlasting monument, send for the Giant's Dance, which is in Killaraus, a mountain in Ireland. For there is a structure of stones there, which none of this age could raise, without a profound knowledge of the mechanical arts. They are stones of a vast magnitude and wonderful quality; and if they can be placed here, as they are there, round this spot of ground, they will stand forever.

At these words of Merlin, Aurelius burst into laughter, and said, "How is it possible to remove such vast stones from so distant a country, as if Britain was not furnished with stones fit for the work?"

Merlin replied, "I entreat your majesty to forbear vain laughter, for what I say is without vanity. They are mystical stones, and of a medicinal virtue. The giants of old brought them from the farthest coast of Africa, and placed them in Ireland, while they inhabited that country. Their design in this was to make baths in them, when they should be taken with any illness. For their method was to wash the stones, and put their sick into the water, which infallibly cured them. With the like success they cured wounds also, adding only the application of some herbs. There is not a stone there which has not some healing virtue."

When the Britons heard this, they resolved to send for the stones, and to make war upon the people of Ireland if they should offer to detain them. And to accomplish this business, they made choice of Uther Pendragon, who was to be attended with fifteen thousand men. They chose also Merlin himself, by whose direction the whole affair was to be managed. A fleet being therefore got ready, they set sail, and with a fair wind arrived in Ireland.

At that time Gillomanius, a youth of wonderful valour, reigned in Ireland; who, upon the news of the arrival of the Britons in his kingdom, levied a vast army, and marched out against them. And when he had learned the occasion of their coming, he smiled, and said to those about him, "No wonder a cowardly race of people where able to make such devastation in the island of Britain, when the Britons are such brutes and fools. Was ever the like folly heard of? What are the stones of Ireland better than those of Britain, that our kingdom must be put to this disturbance for them? To arms, soldiers, and defend your country; while I have life they shall not take from us the least stone of the Giant's Dance."

Uther, seeing them prepared for a battle, attacked them; nor was it long ere the Britons had the advantage, who, having dispersed and killed the Irish, forced Gillomanius to flee. After the victory they went to the mountain

Killaraus, and arrived at the structure of stones, the sight of which filled them both with joy and admiration. And while they were all standing round them, Merlin came up to them and said, "Now try your forces, young men, and see whether strength or art can do the most towards taking down these stones." At this word they all set to their engines with one accord, and attempted the removing of the Giant's Dance. Some prepared cables, others small ropes, others ladders for the work, but all to no purpose.

Merlin laughed at their vain efforts, and then began his own contrivances. When he had placed in order the engines that were necessary, he took down the stones with an incredible facility, and gave directions for carrying them to the ships, and placing them therein. This done, they with joy set sail again, to return to Britain, where they arrived with a fair gale, and repaired to the burying place with the stones.

When Aurelius had notice of it, he sent messengers to all parts of Britain, to summon the clergy and people together to the mount of Ambrius, in order to celebrate with joy and honour the erection of the monument. Upon this summons appeared the bishops, abbots, and people of all other orders and qualities; and upon the day and place appointed for their general meeting, Aurelius placed the crown upon his head, and with royal pomp celebrated the feast of Pentecost, the solemnity whereof he continued the three following days.

In the meantime, all places of honour that were vacant, he bestowed upon his domestics as rewards for their good services. At that time the two metropolitan sees of York and Legions were vacant; and with the general consent of the people, whom he was willing to please in this choice, he granted York to Sanxo, a man of great quality, and much celebrated for his piety; and the City of Legions to Dubricius, whom divine providence had pointed out as a most useful pastor in that place.

As soon as he had settled these and other affairs in the kingdom, he ordered Merlin to set up the stones brought over from Ireland, about the sepulchre; which he accordingly did, and placed them in the same manner as they had been in the mountain Killaraus, and thereby gave a manifest proof of the prevalence of art above strength.

Death of Aurelius Ambrosius

At the same time Pascentius, the son of Vortigern, who had fled over into Germany, was levying all the forces of that kingdom against Aurelius Ambrosius, with a design to revenge his father's death; and promised his men an immense treasure of gold and silver, if with their assistance he could succeed in reducing Britain under his power. When he had at last corrupted all the youth of the country with his large promises, he prepared a vast fleet, and arrived in the northern parts of the island, upon which he began to make great devastations. The king, on the other hand, hearing this news, assembled his army, and marching against them challenged the enraged enemy to a battle; the challenge was accepted, and by the blessing of God the enemy was defeated and put to flight.

Pascentius, after this flight, durst not return to Germany, but shifting his sails, went over to Gillomanius, in Ireland, by whom he was well received. And when he had given him an account of his misfortune, Gillomanius, in pity to him, promised him his assistance, and at the same time vented his complaint of the injuries done him by Uther, the brother of Aurelius, when he came for the Giant's Dance. At last, entering into confederacy together, they made ready their fleet, in which they embarked, and arrived at the city of Menevia.

The news caused Uther Pendragon to levy his forces, and march into Cambria to fight them. For his brother Aurelius then lay sick at Winchester, and was not able to go himself. When Pascentius, Gillomanius, and the Saxons heard of it, they highly rejoiced, flattering themselves that his sickness would facilitate to them the conquest of Britain.

While this occurrence was the subject of the people's discourse, one of the Saxons, named Eopa, came to Pascentius, and said, "What reward will you give the man that shall kill Aurelius Ambrosius for you?" To whom Pascentius answered, "O that I could find a man of such resolution! I would give him a thousand pounds of silver, and my friendship for life; and if by good fortune I can but gain the crown, I promise upon oath to make him a centurion." To this Eopa replied, "I have learned the British language, and know the manners of the people, and have skill in physic. If, therefore, you will perform this promise, I will pretend to be a Christian and a Briton, and when, as a physician, I shall be admitted into the king's presence, I will make him a potion that shall despatch him. And to gain the readier access to him, I will put on the appearance of a devout and learned monk."

Upon this offer, Pascentius entered into covenant with him, and confirmed what he had promised with an oath. Eopa, therefore, shaved his beard and head, and in the habit of a monk hastened to Winchester, loaded with vessels full of medical preparations. As soon as he arrived there, he offered his service to those that attended about the king, and was graciously received by them; for to them nobody was now more acceptable than a physician. Being introduced into the king's presence, he promised to restore him to health, if he would but take his potions. Upon which he had his orders forthwith to prepare one of them, into which when he had secretly conveyed a poisonous mixture, he gave it to the king. As soon as Aurelius had drunk it up, the wicked Ambron ordered him presently to cover himself close up, and fall asleep, that the detestable poison might the better operate. The king readily obeyed his prescriptions, and in hopes of his speedy recovery fell asleep. But the poison quickly diffused itself through all the pores and veins of his body, so that the sleep ended in death.

In the meantime the wicked traitor, having cunningly withdrawn himself first from one and then from another, was no longer to be found in the court. During these transactions at Winchester, there appeared a star of wonderful magnitude and brightness, darting forth a ray, at the end of which was a globe of fire in form of a dragon, out of whose mouth issued forth two rays; one of which seemed to stretch out itself beyond the extent of Gaul, the other towards the Irish Sea, and ended in seven lesser rays.

At the appearance of this star, a general fear and amazement seized his people; and even Uther, the king's brother, who was then upon his march with his army into Cambria, being not a little terrified at it, was very curious to know of the learned men, what it portended. Among others, he ordered Merlin to be called, who also attended in this expedition to give his advice in the management of the war; and who, being now presented before him, was commanded to discover to him the significance of the star.

At this he burst out into tears, and with a loud voice cried out, "O irreparable loss! O distressed people of Britain! Alas! the illustrious prince is departed! The renowned king of the Britons, Aurelius Ambrosius, is dead! whose death will prove fatal to us all, unless God be our helper. Make haste, therefore, most noble Uther, make haste to engage the enemy: the victory will be yours, and you shall be king of all Britain. For the star, and the fiery dragon under it, signifies yourself, and the ray extending towards the Gallic coast portends that you shall have a most potent son, to whose power all those kingdoms shall be subject over which the ray reaches. But the other ray signifies a daughter, whose sons and grandsons shall successively enjoy the kingdom of Britain."

Uther, though he doubted the truth of what Merlin had declared, pursued his march against the enemy, for he was no come within half a day's march of Menevia. When Gillomanius, Pascentius, and the Saxons were informed of his approach, they went out to give him battle. As soon as they were come within sight of each other, both armies began to form themselves into several bodies, and then advanced in a close attack, in which both sides suffered a loss of men, as usually happens in such engagements. At last, towards the close of the day, the advantage was on

Uther's side, and the death of Gillomanius and Pascentius made a way for complete victory. So that the barbarians, being put to flight, hastened to their ships, but were slain by their pursuers.

Thus, by the favour of Christ, the general had triumphant success, and then with all possible expedition, after so great a fatigue, returned back to Winchester: for he had now been informed, by messengers that arrived, of the king's sad fate, and of his burial by the bishops of the country, near the convent of Ambrius, within the Giant's Dance, which in his lifetime he had commanded to be made. For upon hearing the sad news of his death, the bishops, abbots, and all the clergy of that province, had met together at Winchester, to solemnize his funeral. And because in his lifetime he had given orders for his being buried in the sepulchre which he had prepared, and therefore carried his corpse thither, and performed his exsequies with royal magnificence.

Chapter 4: King Uther Pendragon

Victory Over the Saxons

But Uther his brother, having assembled the clergy of the kingdom, took the crown, and by universal consent was advanced to the kingdom. And remembering the explanation which Merlin had made of the star above-mentioned, he commanded two dragons to be made of gold, in likeness of the dragon which he had seen at the ray of the star. As soon as they were finished, which was done with a wonderful nicety of workmanship, he made a present of one the cathedral church of Winchester, but reserved the other for himself, to be carried along with him to his wars. From this time, therefore, he was called Uther Pendragon, which in the British tongue signifies the dragon's head; the occasion of this appellation being Merlin's predicting, from the appearance of a dragon, that he should be king.

In the meantime Octa the son of Hengist, and his kinsman Eosa, seeing they were no longer bound by the treaty which they had made with Aurelius Ambrosius, began to raise disturbances against the king, and infest his countries. For they were now joining with the Saxons whom Pascentius had brought over, and sending messengers into Germany for the rest. Being therefore attended with a vast army, he invaded the northern provinces, and in an outrageous manner destroyed all the cities and fortified places, from Albania to York.

At last, as he was beginning the siege of that city, Uther Pendragon came upon him with the whole power of the kingdom, and gave him battle. The Saxons behaved with great gallantry, and having sustained the assaults of the Britons, forced them to fly; and upon this advantage pursued them with slaughter to the mountain Damen, which was as long as they could do it with day-light. The mountain was high, and had a hazel-wood upon the top of it, and about the middle broken and cavernous rocks, which were a harbour to wild beasts. The Britons made up to it, and stayed there all night among the rocks and hazel-bushes.

But as it began to draw towards day, Uther commanded the consuls and princes to be called together, that he might consult with them in what manner to assault the enemy. Whereupon they forthwith appeared before the king, who commanded them to give their advice; and Gorlois, duke of Cornwall, had orders to deliver his opinion first, out of regard to his years and great experience. "There is no occasion," said he, "for ceremonies or speeches, while we see that it is still night: but there is for boldness and courage, if you desire any longer enjoyment of your life and liberty. The pagans are very numerous, and eager to fight, and we much inferior to them in number; so that if we stay till daybreak, we cannot, in my opinion, attack them to advantage. Come on, therefore, while we have the favour of the night, let us go down in a close body, and surprise them in their camp with a sudden assault. There can be no doubt of success, if with one consent we fall upon them boldly, while they think themselves secure, and have no expectation of our coming in such a manner."

The king and all that were present, were pleased with his advice, and pursued it. For as soon as they were armed and placed in their ranks, they made towards the enemies' camp, designing a general assault. But upon approaching to it, they were discovered by the watch, who with sound of trumpet awaked their companions. The enemies being hereupon put into confusion and astonishment, part of them hastened towards the sea, and part of them ran up and down whithersoever their fear or precipitation drove them. The Britons, finding their coming discovered, hastened their march, and keeping still close together in their ranks, assailed the camp; into which when they had found an entrance, they ran with their drawn swords upon the enemy; who in this sudden surprise made but a faint defence against their vigorous and regular attack; and pursuing this blow with great eagerness they destroyed some thousands of the pagans, took Octa and Eosa prisoners, and entirely dispersed the Saxons.

Uther Deceives Igerna

After this victory Uther repaired to the city of Alclud, where he settled the affairs of that province, and restored peace everywhere. He also made a progress round all the countries of the Scots, and tamed the fierceness of that rebellious people, by such a strict administration of his justice, as none of his predecessors had exercised before: so that in his time offenders were everywhere under great terror, since they were sure of being punished without mercy. At last, when he had established peace in the northern provinces, he went to London, and commanded Octa and Eosa to be kept in prison there.

The Easter following he ordered all the nobility in the kingdom to meet at that city, in order to celebrate that great festival, in honour of which he designed to wear his crown. The summons was everywhere obeyed, and there was a great concourse from all cities to celebrate the day. So the king observed the festival with great solemnity, as he had designed, and very joyfully entertained his nobility, of whom there was a very great muster, with their wives and daughters, suitably to the magnificence of the banquet prepared for them. And having been received with joy by the king, they also expressed the same in their deportment before him.

Among the rest was present Gorlois, duke of Cornwall, with his wife Igerna, the greatest beauty in all Britain. No sooner had the king cast his eyes upon her among the rest of the ladies, than he fell passionately in love with her, and little regarding the rest, made her the subject of all his thoughts. She was the only lady that he continually served with fresh dishes, and to whom he sent golden cups by his confidants; on her he bestowed all his smiles, and to her addressed all his discourse. The husband, discovering this, fell into a great rage, and retired from the court without taking leave: nor was there any body that could stop him, while he was under fear of losing the chief object of his delight. Uther, therefore, in great wrath commanded him to return back to court, and make him satisfaction for this affront. But Gorlois refused to obey; upon which the king was highly incensed, and swore he would destroy his country, if he did not speedily compound for his offence.

Accordingly, without delay, while their anger was hot against each other, the king got together a great army, and marched into Cornwall, the cities and towns thereof he set on fire. But Gorlois durst not engage with him, on account of the inferiority of his numbers; and thought it a wiser course to fortify his towns till he could get succour from Ireland. And as he was under more concern for his wife than himself, he put her into the town of Tintagel, upon the sea-shore, which he looked upon as a place of great safety. But he himself entered the castle of Dimilioc, to prevent their being both at once involved in the same danger, if any should happen.

The king, informed of this, went to the town where Gorlois was, which he besieged, and shut up all the avenues to it. A whole week was now past, when, retaining in mind his love to Igerna, he said to one of his confidants, named Ulfin de Ricaradoch:

"My passion for Igerna is such that I can neither have ease of mind, nor health of body, till I obtain her: and if you cannot assist me with your advice how to accomplish my desire, the inward torments I endure will kill me."

—"Who can advise you in this matter," said Ulfin, "when no force will enable us to have access to her in the town of Tintagel? For it is situated upon the sea, and on every side surrounded by it; and there is but one entrance into it, and that through a straight rock, which three men shall be able to defend against the whole power of the kingdom. Notwithstanding, if the prophet Merlin would in earnest set about this attempt, I am of opinion, you might with his advice obtain your wishes."

The king readily believed what he was so well inclined to, and ordered Merlin, who was also come to the siege, to be called. Merlin, therefore, being introduced into the king's presence, was commanded to give his advice, how the king might accomplish his desire with respect to Igerna. And he, finding the great anguish of the king, was moved by such excessive love, and said, "To accomplish your desire, you must make use of such arts as have not been heard of in your time. I know how, by the force of my medicines, to give you the exact likeness of Gorlois, so that in all respects you shall seem to be no other than himself. If you will therefore obey my prescriptions, I will meta-morphose you into the true semblance of Gorlois, and Ulfin into Jordan of Tintagel, his familiar friend; and I myself, being transformed into another shape, will make the third in the adventure; and in this disguise you may go safely to the town where Igerna is, and have admittance to her."

The king complied with the proposal, and acted with great caution in this affair; and when he had committed the care of the siege to his intimate friends, underwent the medical applications of Merlin, by whom he was transformed into the likeness of Gorlois; as was Ulfin also into Jordan, and Merlin himself into Bricel; so that nobody could see any remains now of their former likeness.

They then set forward on their way to Tintagel, at which they arrived in the evening twilight, and forthwith signified to the porter, that the consul was come; upon which the gates were opened, and the men let in. For what room could there be for suspicion, when Gorlois himself seemed to be there present? The king therefore stayed that night with Igerna, and had the full enjoyment of her, for she was deceived with the false disguise which he had put on, and the artful and amourous discourses wherewith he entertained her. He told her he had left his own place besieged, purely to provide for the safety of her dear self, and the town she was in; so that believing all that he said, she refused him nothing which he desired.

The same night therefore she conceived the most renowned Arthur, whose heroic and wonderful actions have justly rendered his name famous to posterity.

In the meantime, as soon as the king's absence was discovered at the siege, his army unadvisedly made an assault upon the walls, and provoked the besieged count to a battle, who himself also, acting as inconsiderately as they, sallied forth with his men, thinking with such a small handful to oppose a powerful army; but happened to be killed in the very first brunt of the fight, and had all his men routed. The town also was taken; but all the riches of it were not shared equally among the besiegers, but every one greedily took what he could get, according as fortune or his own strength favoured him.

After this bold attempt, came messengers to Igerna, with the news both of the duke's death, and of the event of the siege. But when they saw the king in the likeness of the consul, sitting close by her, they were struck with shame and astonishment at his safe arrival there, whom they had left dead at the siege; for they were wholly ignorant of the miracles which Merlin had wrought with his medicines.

The king therefore smiled at the news, and embracing the countess, said to her: "Your own eyes may convince you that I am not dead, but alive. But notwithstanding, the destruction of the town, and the slaughter of my men, is what very much grieves me, so that there is reason to fear the king's coming upon us, and taking us in this place. To prevent which, I will go out to meet him, and make my peace with him, for fear of a worse disaster."

Accordingly, as soon as he was out of the town, he went to his army, and having put off the disguise of Gorlois, was Uther Pendragon again. Then he returned to the town of Tintagel, which he took, and in it, what he impatiently wished for, Igerna herself. After this they continued to live together with much affection for each other, and had a son and daughter, whose names were Arthur and Anne.

The Saxon Fleet

In the process of time the king was taken ill of a lingering distemper, and meanwhile the keepers of the prison, wherein Octa and Eosa (as we related before) led a weary life, had fled over with them into Germany, and occasioned great fear over the kingdom. For there was a report of their great levies in Germany, and the vast fleet which they had prepared for their return to destroy the island: which the event verified. For they returned in a great fleet, and with a prodigious number of men, and invaded the parts of Albania, where they destroyed both cities and inhabitants with fire and sword.

Wherefore, in order to repulse the enemies, the command of the British army was committed to Lot of Londonesia, who was a consul, and a most valiant knight, and grown up to maturity both of years and wisdom. Out of respect to his eminent merits, the king had given him his daughter Anne, and entrusted him with the care of the kingdom, during his illness. In his expedition against the enemies he had various success, being often repulsed by them, and forced to retreat to the cities; but he oftener routed and dispersed them, and compelled them to flee sometimes into the woods, sometimes to their ships. So that in a war attended with so many turns of fortune, it was hard to know which side had the better. The greatest injury to the Britons was their own pride, in disdaining to obey the consul's commands; for which reason all their efforts against the enemy were less vigourous and successful.

The island being by this conduct now almost laid waste, the king, having information of the matter, fell into a greater rage than his weakness could bear, and commanded all his nobility to come before him, that he might reprove them severely for their pride and cowardice. And as soon as they were all entered into his presence, he sharply rebuked them in menacing language, and swore he himself would lead them against the enemy. For this purpose he ordered a horse-litter to be made, in which he designed to be carried, for his infirmity would not suffer him to use any other sort of vehicle; and he charged them to be all ready to march against the enemy at the first opportunity. So, without delay, the horse-litter and all his attendants were got ready and the day arrived which had been appointed for their march.

The king, therefore, being put into his vehicle, they marched directly to Verulam, where the Saxons were grievously oppressing the people. When Octa and Eosa had intelligence that the Britons were come, and that the king was brought in a horse-litter, they disdained to fight with him, saying, it would be a shame for such brave men to fight with one that was half dead. For which reason they retired into the city, and, as it were in contempt of any danger from the enemy, left their gates wide open.

But Uther, upon information of this, instantly commanded his men to lay siege to the city, and assault the walls on all sides; which orders they strictly executed; and were just entering the breaches which they had made in the walls, and ready to begin a general assault, when the Saxons, seeing the advantages which the Britons had gained, and being forced to abate somewhat of their haughty pride, condescended so far as to put themselves into a posture of defence. They therefore mounted the walls, from whence they poured down showers of arrows, and repulsed the Britons.

On both sides the contest continued till night released them from the fatigue of their arms, which was what many of the Britons desired, though the greater part of them were for having the matter quickly decided with the enemy. The Saxons, on the other hand, finding how prejudicial their own pride had been to them, and that the advantage was on the side of the Britons, resolved to make a sally at break of day, and try their fortune with the enemy in the open field; which accordingly was done. For no sooner was it daylight, than they marched out with this design, all in their proper ranks. The Britons, seeing them, divided their men into several bodies, and advancing towards them, began the attack first, their part being to assault, while the others were only upon the defensive. However, much blood was shed on both sides, and the greatest part of the day spent in the fight, when at last, Octa and Eosa being killed, the Saxons turned their backs, and left the Britons a complete victory.

The king at this was in such an ecstasy of joy, that whereas before he could hardly raise up himself without the help of others, he now without any difficulty sat upright in his horse-litter of himself, as if he was on a sudden restored to health; and said with a laughing and merry countenance, "These Ambrons called me the half-dead king, because my sickness obliged me to lie on a horse-litter; and indeed so I was. Yet victory to me half-dead, is better than to be safe and sound and vanquished. For to die with honour is preferable to living with disgrace."

The Death of Uther

The Saxons, notwithstanding this defeat, persisted in their malice, and entering the northern provinces, without respire infested the people there. Uther's purpose was to have pursued them, but his princes dissuaded him from it, because his illness had increased since the victory. This gave new courage to the enemy, who left nothing unattempted to make conquest of the kingdom.

And now they have recourse to their former treacherous practices, and contrive how to compass the king's death by secret villainy. And because they could have no access to him otherwise, they resolved to take him off by poison; in which they succeeded. For while he was lying ill at Verulam, they sent away some spies in a poor habit, to learn the state of the court; and when they had thoroughly informed themselves of the posture of affairs, they found out an expedient by which they might accomplish their villainy. For there was near the court a spring of very clear water, which the king used to drink of, when his distemper had made all other liquors nauseous to him. This the detestable conspirators made use of to destroy him, by so poisoning the whole mass of water which sprang up, that the next time the king drank of it, he was seized with sudden death, as were also a hundred other persons after him, till the villainy was discovered, and a heap of earth thrown over the well.

As soon as the king's death was divulged, the bishops and clergy of the kingdom assembled, and carried his body to the convent of Ambrius, where they buried it with regal solemnity, close by Aurelius Ambrosius, within the Giant's Dance.

Chapter 5: Arthur Becomes King

Arthur Is Crowned

Uther Pendragon being dead, the nobility from several provinces assembled together at Silchester, and proposed to Dubricius, archbishop of Legions, that he should consecrate Arthur, Uther's son, to be their king.

For they were now in great straits, because, upon hearing of the king's death, the Saxons had invited over their countrymen from Germany, and, under the command of Colgrin, were attempting to exterminate the whole British race. They had also entirely subdued all that part of the island which extends from the Humber to the sea of Caithness.

Dubricius, therefore, grieving for the calamities of his country, in conjunction with the other bishops, set the crown upon Arthur's head.

Arthur was then fifteen years old, but a youth of such

unparalleled courage and generosity, joined with that sweetness of temper and innate goodness, as gained him universal love. When his coronation was over, he, according to usual custom, showed his bounty and munificence to the people. And such a number of soldiers flocked to him upon it, that his treasury was not able to answer that vast expense. But such a spirit of generosity, joined with valour, can never long want means to support itself.

War with the Saxons

Arthur, therefore, the better to keep up his munificence, resolved to make use of his courage, and to fall upon the Saxons, that he might enrich his followers with their wealth. To this he was also moved by the justice of the cause, since the entire monarchy of Britain belonged to him by hereditary right.

Hereupon assembling the youth under his command, he marched to York, of which, when Colgrin had intelligence, he met him with a very great army, composed of Saxons, Scots and Picts, by the river Duglas; where a battle happened, with the loss of the greater part of both armies.

Notwithstanding, the victory fell to Arthur, who pursued Colgrin to York, and there besieged him. Badulph, upon the news of his brother's flight, went towards the siege with a body of six thousand men, to his relief, for at the time of the battle he was upon the sea-coast, waiting for the arrival of duke Cheldric with succours from Germany.

And being now no more than ten miles distant from the city, his purpose was to make a speedy march in the night-time, and fall upon the enemy by way of surprise.

But Arthur, having intelligence of his design, sent a detachment of six hundred horse, and three thousand foot, under the command of Cador, duke of Cornwall, to meet him the same night. Cador, therefore, falling into the same road along which the enemy was passing, made a sudden assault upon them, and entirely defeated the Saxons, and put them to flight.

Badulph was excessively grieved at this disappointment in the relief which he intended for his brother, and began to think of some other stratagem to gain access to him, in which if he could but succeed, he thought they might concert measures together for their safety. And since he had no other way for it, he shaved his head and beard, and put on the habit of a jester with a harp, and in this disguise walked up and down in the camp, playing upon his instrument as if he had been a harper. He thus passed unsuspected, and by a little and little went up to the walls of the city, where he was at last discovered by the besieged, who thereupon drew him up with cords, and conducted him to his brother. At this unexpected, though much desired meeting, they spent some time in joyfully embracing each other, and then began to consider various stratagems for their delivery.

At last, just as they were considering their case desperate, the ambassadors returned from Germany, and brought with them to Albania a fleet of six hundred sail, laden with brave soldiers, under the command of Cheldric. Upon this news, Arthur was dissuaded by his council from continuing the siege any longer, for fear of hazarding a battle with so powerful and numerous an army.

The Bretons Send Aid

Arthur complied with their advice, and made his retreat to London, where he called an assembly of all the clergy and nobility of the kingdom, to ask their advice, what course to take against the formidable power of the pagans.

After some deliberation, it was agreed that ambassadors should be despatched to Armorica, to king Hoel, to represent to him the calamitous state of Britain. Hoel was the son of Arthur's sister by Dubricius, king of the Armorican Britons; so that, upon the advice of the disturbances his uncle was threatened with, he ordered his fleet to be got ready, and, having assembled fifteen thousand men, he arrived with the first fair wind at Hamo's Port, and was received with all suitable honour by Arthur, and most affectionately embraced by him.

After a few days they went to relieve the city Kaerliudcoit, that was besieged by the pagans; which being situated upon a mountain, between two rivers in the province of Lindisia, is called by another name Lindocolinum.

As soon as they arrived there with all their forces, they fought with the Saxons, and made a grievous slaughter of them, to the number of six thousand; part of whom were drowned in the rivers, part fell by the hands of the Britons. The rest in a great consternation quitted the siege and fled, but were closely pursued by Arthur, till they came to the wood of Celidon, where they endeavoured to form themselves into a body again, and make a stand. And here they again joined battle with the Britons, and made a brave defence, whilst the trees that were in the place secured them against the enemies' arrows.

Arthur, seeing this, commanded the trees that were in that part of the wood to be cut down, and the trunks to be placed quite round them, so as to hinder their getting out; resolving to keep them pent up here till he could reduce them by famine. He then commanded his troops to besiege the wood, and continued three days in that place.

The Saxons, having now no provisions to sustain them, and being just ready to starve with hunger, begged for leave to go out; in consideration whereof they offered to leave all their gold and silver behind them, and return back to Germany with nothing but their empty ships. They promised also that they would pay him tribute from Germany, and leave hostages with him. Arthur, after consultation about it, granted their petition, allowing them only leave to depart, and retaining all their treasures, as also hostages for payment of the tribute.

But as they were under sail on their return home, they repented of their bargain, and tacked about again towards Britain, and went on shore at Totness. No sooner were they landed, than they made an utter devastation of the country as far as the Severn sea, and put all the peasants to the sword. From thence they pursued their furious march to the town of Bath, and laid siege to it.

When the king had intelligence of it, he was beyond measure surprised at their proceedings, and immediately gave orders for the execution of the hostages. And desisting from an attempt which he had entered upon to reduce the Scots and Picts, he marched with the utmost expedition to raise the siege; but laboured under very great difficulties, because he had left his nephew Hoel sick at Alclud.

Defeat of the Saxons

At length, having entered the province of Somerset, and beheld how the siege was carried on, he addressed himself to his followers in these words: "Since these impious and detestable Saxons have disdained to keep faith with me, I, to keep faith in God, will endeavour to revenge the blood of my countrymen this day upon them. To arms, soldiers, and courageously fall upon the perfidious wretches, over whom we shall, with Christ assisting us, undoubtedly obtain the victory."

When he had done speaking, St. Dubricius, archbishop of Legions, going to the top of a hill, cried out with a loud voice, "You that have the honour to profess the Christian faith, keep fixed in your minds the love which you owe to your country and fellow subjects, whose sufferings by the treachery of the pagans will be an everlasting reproach to you, if you do not courageously defend them. It is your country which you fight for, and for which you should, when required, voluntarily suffer death; for that itself is victory and the cure of the soul. For he that shall die for his brethren, offers himself as a living sacrifice to God, and has Christ for his example, who condescended to lay down his life for his brethren. If therefore any of you shall be killed in this war, that death itself, which is suffered in so glorious a cause, shall be to him for penance and absolution of all his sins."

At these words, all of them, encouraged with the benediction of the holy prelate, instantly armed themselves, and prepared to obey his orders. Also Arthur himself, having put on a coat of mail suitable to the grandeur of so powerful a king, placed a golden helmet on his head, on which was engraved the figure of a dragon; and on his shoulders his shield called Priwen; upon which the picture of the blessed Mary, mother of God, was painted, in order to put him frequently in mind of her. Then girding on his Caliburn, which was an excellent sword made in the isle of Avallon, he graced his right hand with his lance, named Ron, which was hard, broad, and fit for slaughter.

After this, having placed his men in order, he boldly attacked the Saxons, who were drawn out in the shape of a wedge, as their manner was. And they, notwithstanding that the Britons fought with great eagerness, made a noble defence all that day; but at length, towards sunsetting, climbed up the next mountain, which served them for a camp: for they desired no larger extent of ground, since they confided very much in their numbers.

The next morning Arthur, with his army, went up the mountain, but lost many of his men in the ascent, by the advantage which the Saxons had in their station on the top, from whence they could pour down upon him with much greater speed, than he was able to advance against them. Notwithstanding, after a very hard struggle, the Britons gained the summit of the hill, and quickly came to a close engagement with the enemy, who again gave them a warm reception, and made a vigorous defence.

In this manner was a great part of that day also spent, whereupon Arthur, provoked to see the little advantage he had yet gained, and that victory still continued in suspense, drew out his Caliburn, and, calling upon the name of the blessed Virgin, rushed forward with great fury into the thickest of the enemy's ranks; of whom (such was the merit of his prayers) not one escaped alive that felt the fury of his sword; neither did he give over the fury of his assault until he had, with his Caliburn alone, killed four hundred and seventy men.

The Britons, seeing this, followed their leader in great multitudes, and made slaughter on all sides; so that Colgrin, and Badulph his brother, and many thousands more, fell before them. But Cheldric, in this imminent danger to his men, betook himself to flight.

The victory being thus gained, the king commanded Cador, duke of Cornwall, to pursue them, while he himself should hasten his march into Albania: from whence he had advice that the Scots and Picts were besieging Alclud, in which, as we said before, Hoel lay sick. Therefore he hastened to his assistance, for fear he might fall into the hands of the barbarians.

In the meantime the duke of Cornwall, who had the command of ten thousand men, would not as yet pursue the Saxons in their flight, but speedily made himself master of their ships, to hinder their getting on board, and manned them with his best soldiers, who were to beat back the pagans in case they should flee thither: after this he hastily pursued the enemy, according to Arthur's command, and allowed no quarter to those he could overtake. So that they whose behaviour before was so cruel and insolent, now with timorous hearts fled for shelter, sometimes to the coverts of the woods, sometimes to mountains and caves, to prolong a wretched life. At last, when none of these places could afford them a safe retreat, they entered the Isle of Thanet with their broken forces; but neither did they there get free from the duke of Cornwall's pursuit, for he still continued slaughtering them, and gave them no respite till he had killed Cheldric, and taken hostages for the surrender of the rest.

Defeat of the Scots and Picts

Having therefore settled peace here, he directed his march to Alclud, which Arthur had relieved from the oppression of the barbarians, and from thence conducted his army to Mureif, where the Scots and Picts were besieged; after three several battles with the king and his nephew, they had fled as far as this province, and entering upon the lake Lumond, sought for refuge in the islands that are upon it.

This lake contains sixty islands, and receives sixty rivers into it, which empty themselves into the sea by no more than one mouth. There is also an equal number of rocks in these islands, as also of eagles' nests in those rocks, which flocked together there every year, and, by the loud and general noise which they now made, foreboded some remarkable event that should happen to the kingdom.

To these islands, therefore, had the enemy fled, thinking the lake would serve them instead of a fortification, but it proved of little advantage to them. For

Arthur, having got together a fleet, sailed round the rivers, and besieged the enemy fifteen days together, by which they were so straitened with hunger, that they died by thousands.

While he was harassing them in this manner Guillamurius, king of Ireland, came up in a fleet with a very great army of barbarians, in order to relieve the besieged. This obliged Arthur to raise the siege, and turn his arms against the Irish, whom he slew without mercy, and compelled the rest to return back to their country.

After this victory, he proceeded in his first attempt, which was to extirpate the whole race of the Scots and Picts, and treated them with an unparalleled severity. And as he allowed quarter to none, the bishops of that miserable country, with all the inferior clergy, met together, and bearing the reliques of the saints and other consecrated things of the church before them, barefooted, came to implore the king's mercy for their people.

As soon as they were admitted into his presence, they fell down upon their knees, and humbly besought him to have pity on their distressed country, since the sufferings which he had already made it undergo, were sufficient; nor was there any necessity to cut off the small remainder to a man; and that he would allow them the enjoyment of a small part of the country, since they were willing to bear the yoke which he should impose upon them.

The king was moved at the manner of their delivering this petition, and could not forbear expressing his clemency to them with tears; and at the request of those holy men, granted them pardon.

Wonderful Ponds

This affair being concluded, Hoel had the curiosity to view the situation of the lake, and wondered to find the number of rivers, islands, rocks, and eagles' nests, so exactly correspond: and while he was reflecting upon it as something that appeared miraculous, Arthur came to him, and told him of another pond in the same province, which was yet more wonderful. For not far from thence was one whose length and breadth were each twenty feet, and depth five feet. But whether its square figure was natural or artificial, the wonder of it was, there were four different sorts of fishes in the four several corners of it, none of which were ever found in any other part of the pond but their own.

He told him likewise of another pond in Wales, near the Severn, called by the people Linligwan, into which when the sea flows, it receives it in the manner of a gulf, but so as to swallow up the tide, and never be filled, or have its banks covered by it. But at the ebbing of the sea, it throws out the waters which it had swallowed, as high as a mountain, and at last dashes and covers the banks with them. In the meantime, if all the people of that country should stand near with their faces towards it, and happened to have their clothes sprinkled with the dashing of the waves, they would hardly, if at all, escape being swallowed up by the pond. But with their backs towards it, they need not fear being dashed, though they stood upon the very banks.

Chapter 6: The Golden Age

Britain Restored

The king, after his general pardon granted to the Scots, went to York to celebrate the feast of Christ's nativity, which was now at hand.

On entering the city, he beheld with grief the desolation of the churches; for upon the expulsion of the holy Archbishop Sanxo, and all of the clergy there, the temples of which were half burned down, had no longer divine service performed in them: so much had the impious rage of the pagans prevailed.

After this, in an assembly of the clergy and the people, he appointed Pyramus his chaplain metropolitan of that see. The churches that lay level with the ground, he rebuilt, and (which was their chief ornament) saw them filled with assemblies of devout persons of both sexes. Also the nobility that were driven out by the disturbances of the Saxons, he restored to their country.

There were three brothers of royal blood, viz. Lot, Urian, and Augusel, who, before the Saxons had prevailed, held the government of those parts. Being willing therefore to bestow on these, as he did on others, the rights of their ancestors, he restored to Augusel the sovereignty over the Scots; his brother Urian he honoured with the sceptre of Mureif; and Lot, who in the time of Aurelius Ambrosius had married his sister, by whom he had two sons, Walgan and Modred, he reestablished in the consulship of Londonesia, and the other provinces belonging to him.

At length, when the whole country was reduced by him to its ancient state, he took to wife Guanhumara,[6] descended from a noble family of Romans, who was educated under duke Cador, and in beauty surpassed all the women of the island.

Conquests Abroad

The next summer he fitted out a fleet, and made an expedition into Ireland, which he was desirous to reduce.

Upon landing there, he was met by king Guillamurius before mentioned, with a vast number of men, who came with a design to fight him; but at the very beginning of the battle, those naked and unarmed people were miserably routed, and fled to such places as lay open to them for

---

[6] Guanhumara is Geoffrey's Latin rendering of Guinevere. Gwenhwyfar is the Welsh spelling.

shelter. Guillamurius also in a short time was taken prisoner, and forced to submit; as were also all the other princes of the country after the king's example, being under great consternation at what had happened.

After an entire conquest of Ireland, he made a voyage with his fleet to Iceland, which he also subdued.

And now a rumour spreading over the rest of the islands, that no country was able to withstand him, Doldavius, king of Gothland, and Gunfasius, king of the Orkneys, came voluntarily, and made their submission, on a promise of paying tribute.

Arthur Triumphant

Then, as soon as winter was over, he returned back to Britain, where having established the kingdom, he resided in it for twelve years together in peace.

After this, having invited over to him all persons whatsoever that were famous for valour in foreign nations, he began to augment the number of his domestics, and introduced such politeness into his court, as people of the remotest countries thought worthy of their imitation. So that there was not a nobleman who thought himself worthy of any consideration, unless his clothes and arms were made in the same fashion as those Arthur's knights.

At length the fame of his munificence and valour spreading over the whole world, he became a terror to the kings of other countries, who grievously feared the loss of their dominions, if he should make any attempt upon them. Being much perplexed with these anxious cares, they repaired their cities and towers, and built towns in convenient places, the better to fortify themselves against any enterprise of Arthur, when occasion should require.

Arthur, being informed of what they were doing, was delighted to find how much they stood in awe of him, and formed a design for the conquest of all Europe.

Then having prepared his fleet, he first attempted Norway, that he might procure the crown of it for Lot, his sister's husband. This Lot was the nephew of Sichelin, king of the Norwegians, who being then dead, had appointed him his successor in the kingdom. But the Norwegians, disdaining to receive him, had advanced one Riculf to the sovereignty, and having fortified their cities, thought they were able to oppose Arthur. Walgan, the son of Lot, was then a youth twelve years old, and was recommended by his uncle to the service of pope Supplicius, from whom he received arms.

But to return to the history: as soon as Arthur arrived on the coast of Norway, king Riculf, attended with the whole power of that kingdom, met him, and gave him battle, in which, after a great loss of blood on both sides, the Britons at length had the advantage, and making a vigorous charge, killed Riculf and many others with him. Having thus defeated them, they set the cities on fire, dispersed the country people, and pursued the victory till they had reduced all Norway, as also Dacia, under the dominion of Arthur.

After the conquest of these countries, and establishment of Lot upon the throne of Norway, Arthur made a voyage to Gaul, and dividing his army into several bodies, began to lay waste that country on all sides. The province of Gaul was then committed to Flollo, a Romen tribune, who held the government of it under the emperor Leo. Upon intelligence of Arthur's coming, he raised all the forces that were under his command, and made war against him, but without success. For Arthur was attended with the youth of all the islands that he had subdued; for which reason he was reported to have such an army as was thought invincible. And even the greater part of the Gallic army, encouraged by his bounty, came over to his service.

Therefore Flollo, seeing the disadvantages he lay under, left his camp, and fled with a small number to Paris. There having recruited his army, he fortified the city, and resolved to stand another engagement with Arthur. But while he was thinking of strengthening himself with auxiliary forces in the neighbouring countries, Arthur came upon him unawares, and besieged him in the city.

When a month had passed, Flollo, with grief observing his people perish with hunger, sent a message to Arthur, that they two alone should decide the conquest for the kingdom in a duel: for being a person of great stature, boldness and courage, he gave this challenge in confidence of success. Arthur was extremely pleased at Flollo's proposal, and sent him word back again, that he would give him the meeting which he desired. A treaty, therefore, bring on both sides agreed to, they met together in the island without the city, where the people waited to see the event.

They were both gracefully armed, and mounted on admirably swift horses; and it was hard to tell which gave the greater hopes of victory. When they had presented themselves against each other with their lances aloft, they put spurs to their horses, and began a fierce encounter. But Arthur, who handled his lance more warily, struck it into the upper part of Flollo's breast, and avoiding his enemy's weapon, laid him prostrate upon the ground, and was just going to despatch him with his drawn sword, when Flollo, starting up on a sudden, met him with his lance couched, wherewith he mortally stabbed the breast of Arthur's horse, and caused both him and his rider to fall.

The Britons, when they saw their king lying on the ground, fearing he was killed, could hardly be restrained from breach of covenant, and falling with one consent upon the Gauls. But just as they were upon rushing into the lists, Arthur hastily got up, and guarding himself with his shield, advanced with speed against Flollo. And now they renewed the assault with great rage, eagerly bent upon one another's destruction. At length Flollo, watching his advantage, gave Arthur a blow on the forehead, which might have proved mortal, had he not blunted the edge of his weapon against the helmet.

When Arthur saw his coat of mail and shield red with blood, he was inflamed with still greater rage, and lifting up his Caliburn with his utmost strength struck it through the helmet into Flollo's head, and made a terrible gash. With this wound Flollo fell down, tearing the ground with his spurs, and expired. As soon as this news was spread through the army, the citizens ran together, and opening the gates, surrendered the city to Arthur.

After this victory, he divided his army into two parts; one of which he committed to the conduct of Hoel, whom he ordered to march against Guitard, commander of the Pictavians; while he with the other part should endeavour to reduce the other provinces. Hoel upon this entered Aquitaine, possessed himself of the cities of that country, and after distressing Guitard in several battles, forced him to surrender. He also destroyed Gascony with fire and sword, and subdued the princes of it.

At the end of nine years, in which time all the parts of Gaul were entirely reduced, Arthur returned back to Paris, where he kept his court, and calling an assembly of the clergy and people, established peace and the just administration of the laws in that kingdom. Then he bestowed Neustria, now called Normandy, upon Bedver,[7] his butler; the province of Andegavia upon Caius,[8] his steward; and several other provinces upon his great men that attended him. Thus having settled the peace of the cities and countries there, he returned back in the beginning of spring to Britain.

A Festival

Upon the approach of the feast of Pentecost, Arthur, the better to demonstrate his joy after such triumphal success, and for the more solemn observation of that festival, and reconciling the minds of the princes that were now subject to him, resolved, during that season, to hold a magnificent court, to place the crown upon his head, and to invite all the kings and dukes under his subjection, to the solemnity.

[7] In later versions of the legend, this name was spelled Bedivere.
[8] In later versions, this name was shortened to Kay.

And when he had communicated his design to his familiar friends, he pitched upon the City of Legions as a proper place for his purpose. For besides its great wealth above the other cities, its situation, which was in Glamorganshire upon the river Usk, near the Severn sea, was most pleasant, and fit for so great a solemnity. For on one side it was washed by that noble river, so that the kings and princes from the countries beyond the seas might have the convenience of sailing up to it. On the other side, the beauty of the meadows and groves, and magnificence of the royal palaces with lofty gilded roofs that adorned it, made it even rival the grandeur of Rome. It was also famous for two churches; whereof one was built in honour of the martyr Julius and adorned with a choir of virgins, who had devoted themselves wholly to the service of God; but the other, which was founded in memory of St. Aaron, his companion, and maintained a convent of canons, was the third metropolitan church of Britain. Besides, there was a college of two hundred philosophers, who, being learned in astronomy and the other arts, were diligent in observing the courses of the stars, and gave Arthur true predictions of the events that would happen at that time.

In this place, therefore, which afforded such delights, were preparations made for the ensuing festival. Ambassadors were then sent into several kingdoms, to invite to court the princes both of Gaul and all the adjacent islands.

Accordingly came Augusel, king of Albania, now Scotland; Urian, king of Mureif; Cadwallo Lewirh, king of the Venedotians, now called the North Wales men; Sater, king of the Demetians, or South Wales men; Cador, king of

Cornwall, also the archbishops of the three metropolitan sees, London, York, and Dubricius of the City of Legions. This prelate, who was primate of Britain, and legate of the apostolical see, was so eminent for his piety that he could cure any sick person by his prayers.

There came also the consuls of the principal cities, viz. Morvid, consul of Gloucester; Mauron, of Worcester; Anaraut, of Salisbury; Arthgal, of Cargueit or Wargueit; Jugein, of Legecester; Cursalen, of Kaicester; Kinmare, duke of Dorobernia; Galluc, of Salisbury; Urgennius, of Bath; Jonathal, of Dorchester; Boso, of Ridoc,, that is, Oxford. Besides the consuls, came the following worthies of no less dignity: Danaut map Papo, Cheneus map Coil; Peredur map Eridur; Guiful map Nogoit; Regin map Claut; Eddelein map Cledauc; Kincar map Bagan; Kimmare; Gorboroniam map Goit; Clofaut; Rupmaneton; Kimbelim map Trunat; Cathleus map Catel; Kinlich map Neton; and many others too tedious to enumerate.

From the adjacent islands came Guillamurius, king of Ireland; Malvasius, king of Iceland; Doldavius, king of Gothland; Gunfasius, king of the Orkneys; Lot, king of Norway; Aschillius, king of the Dacians.

From the parts beyond the seas, came Holdin king of Ruteni; Leodegarius, consul of Bolonia; Bedver, the butler, duke of Normandy; Borellus of Cenomania; Caius, the steward, duke of Andegavia; Guitard, of Pictavia; also the twelve peers of Gaul, whom Guerinus Carnotensis brought along with him; Hoel, duke of the Armorican Britons, and his nobility, who came with such a train of mules, horses, and rich furniture, as it is difficult to describe.

Besides these, there remained no prince of any

consideration on this side of Spain, who came not upon this invitation. And no wonder, when Arthur's munificence, which was celebrated over the whole world, made him beloved by all people.

Coronation Ceremony

When all were assembled together in the city, upon the day of the solemnity, the archbishops were conducted to the palace, in order to place the crown upon the king's head. Therefore Dubricius, inasmuch as the court was kept in his diocese, made himself ready to celebrate the office, and undertook the ordering of whatever related to it.

As soon as the king was invested with his royal habiliments, he was conducted in great pomp to the metropolitan church, supported on each side by two archbishops, and having four kings, viz. of Albania, Cornwall, Demetia, and Venedotia, whose right it was, bearing four golden swords before him.

He was also attended with a concert of all sorts of music, which made most excellent harmony.

On another part was the queen, dressed out in her richest ornaments, conducted by the archbishops and bishops to the Temple of Virgins; the four queens also of the kings last mentioned, bearing before her four white doves according to ancient custom; and after her there followed a retinue of women, making all imaginable demonstrations of joy.

When the whole procession was ended, so transporting was the harmony of the musical instruments and voices, whereof there was a vast variety in both churches, that the knights who attended were in doubt which to prefer, and therefore crowded from the one to the other by turns, and were far from being tired with the solemnity, though the whole day had been spent in it.

At last, when the divine service was over at both churches, the king and queen put off their crowns, and putting on their lighter ornaments, went to the banquet; he to one palace with the men, and she to another with the women. For the Britons still observed the ancient custom of Troy, by which the men and women used to celebrate the festivals apart.

When they had all taken their seats according to precedence, Caius the steward, in rich robes of ermine, with a thousand young noblemen, served up the dishes. From another part, Bedver the butler was followed with the same number of attendants, in various habits, who waited with all kinds of cups and drinking vessels. In the queen's palace were innumerable waiters, dressed with variety of ornaments, all performing their respective offices; which if I should describe particularly, I should draw out the history to a tedious length.

For at that time Britain had arrived at such a pitch of grandeur, that in abundance of riches, luxury of ornaments, and politeness of inhabitants, it far surpassed all other kingdoms. The knights in it that were famous for feats of chivalry, wore their clothes and arms all of the same colour and fashion: and the women also no less celebrated for their wit, wore all the same kind of apparel; and esteemed none worthy of their love, but such as had given a proof of their valour in three several battles. Thus was the valour of the men an encouragement for the women's chastity, and the love of the women a spur to the soldier's bravery.

Sports and Honors

As soon as the banquets were over, they went into the fields without the city, to divert themselves with various sports.

The military men composed a kind of diversion in imitation of a fight on horseback; and the ladies, placed on the top of the walls as spectators, in a sportive manner darted their amorous glances at the courtiers, the more to encourage them. Others spent the remainder of the day in other diversions, such as shooting with bows and arrows, tossing the pike, casting of heavy stones and rocks, playing at dice and the like, and all these inoffensively and without quarrelling. Whoever gained the victory in any of these sports, was rewarded with a rich prize by Arthur.

In this manner were the first three days spent; and on the fourth, all who, upon account of their titles, bore any kind of office at this solemnity, were called together to receive honours and preferments in reward of their services, and to fill up the vacancies in the governments of cities and castles, archbishoprics, bishoprics, abbeys, and other posts of honour.

But St. Dubricius, from a pious desire of leading a hermit's life, made a voluntary resignation of his archiepiscopal dignity; and in his room was consecrated David, the king's uncle, whose life was a perfect example of that goodness which by his doctrine he taught. In place of St. Samson, archbishop of Dole, was appointed, with the consent of Hoel, king of the Armorican Britons, Chelianus, a priest of Llandaff, a person highly recommended for his good life and character. The bishopric of Silchester was conferred on Mauganius, that of Winchester upon Diwanius, and that of Alclud to Eldanius.

Chapter 7: The War with Rome

The Roman Challenge

While he was disposing of these preferments upon them, it happened that twelve men of an advanced age, and venerable aspect, and bearing olive branches in their right hands, for a token that they were come upon an embassy, appeared before the king, moving towards him with a slow pace, and speaking with a soft voice; and after their compliments paid, presented him with a letter from Lucius Tiberius, in these words: —

"Lucius, procurator of the commonwealth, to Arthur, king of Britain, according to his desert. The insolence of your tyranny is what fills me with the highest admiration, and the injuries you have done to Rome still increase my wonder. But it is provoking to reflect, that you are grown so much above yourself, as willfully to avoid seeing this: nor do you consider what it is to have offended by unjust deeds a Senate, to whom you cannot be ignorant the whole world owes vassalage. For the tribute of Britain, which the senate had enjoined you to pay, and which used to be paid to the Roman emperors successively from the time of Julius Caesar, you have had the presumption to withhold, in contempt of their imperial authority. You have seized the province of the Allobroges, and all the islands of the ocean, whose kings, while the Roman power prevailed in those parts, paid tribute to our ancestors. And because the senate have decreed to demand justice of you for such repeated injuries, I command you to appear at Rome before the middle of August the next year, there to make satisfaction to your masters, and undergo such sentence as they shall in justice pass upon you. Which if you refuse to do, I shall come to you, and endeavour to recover with my sword, what you in your madness have robbed us of."

Council of War

As soon as the letter was read in the presence of the king and consuls, Arthur withdrew with them into the Giant's Tower, which was at the entrance to the palace, to think what answer was fit to be returned to such an insolent message.

As they were going up the stairs, Cador, duke of Cornwall, who was a man of a merry disposition, said to the king in a jocose manner: "I have been till now under fear, lest the easy life which the Britons lead, by enjoying a long peace, might make them cowards, and extinguish the fame of their gallantry, by which they have raised their name above all other nations. For where the exercise of arms is wanting, and the pleasures of women, dice, and other diversions take place, no doubt, what remains of virtue, honour, courage, and thirst of praise, will be stained with the rust of idleness. For now almost five years have passed, since we have been abandoned to these delights, and have had no exercise of war. Therefore, to deliver us from sloth, God has stirred up this spirit of the Romans, to restore our military virtues to their ancient state."

In this manner did he entertain them with discourse, till they were come to their seats, on which when they were all placed, Arthur spoke to them after this manner.

"My companions in both good and bad fortune, whose abilities both in counsel and war I have hitherto experienced; the present exigence of affairs, after the message which we have received, requires your careful deliberation and prudent resolutions; for whatever is wisely concerted, is easily executed. Therefore we shall be the better able to bear the annoyance which Lucius threatens to give us, if we unanimously apply ourselves to consider how to overcome it.

"In my opinion we have no great reason to fear him, when we reflect on the unjust pretense on which he demands tribute of us. He says he has a right to it, because it was paid to Julius Caesar, and his successors, who invaded Britain with an army at the invitation of the ancient Britons, when they were quarrelling among themselves, and by force reduced the country under their power, when weakened by civil dissention. And because they gained it in this manner, they had the injustice to take tribute of it. For that can never be possessed justly, which is gained by force and violence. So that he has no reasonable grounds to pretend we are of right his tributaries.

"But since he has the presumption to make an unjust demand of us, we have certainly as good reason to demand of him tribute from Rome; let the longer sword therefore determine the right between us. For if Rome has decreed that tribute ought to paid to it from Britain, on account of it having been formerly under the yoke of Julius Caesar, and other Roman emperors; I for the same reason now decree, that Rome ought to pay tribute to me, because my predecessors formerly held the government of it.

"For Belinus, that glorious king of the Britons, with the assistance of his brother Brennus, duke of the Allobroges, after they had hanged up twenty noble Romans in the middle of the market-place, took their city, and kept possession of it a long time. Likewise Constantine, the son of Helena, and Maximian, who were both my kinsmen, gained the imperial throne of Rome. Do not you, therefore, think that we ought to demand tribute of the Romans? As for Gaul and the adjacent islands of the ocean, we have no occasion to return them any answer, since they did not defend them, when we attempted to free them from their power."

As soon as he had done speaking to this effect, Hoel, king of the Armorican Britons, who had the precedence of the rest, made answer in these words.

"After the most profound deliberation that any of us shall be able to make, I think better advice cannot be given, than what your majesty in your great wisdom and policy now offers. Your speech, which is no less wise than eloquent, has superseded all consultation on our part; and nothing remains for us to do, but to admire and gratefully acknowledge your majesty's firmness of mind, and depth of policy, to which we owe such excellent advice

"For if upon this notice you are pleased to make an expedition to Rome, I doubt not but it will be crowned with glorious success, since it will be undertaken for the defence of our liberties, and to demand justly of our enemies, what they have unjustly demanded of us. For that person who would rob another, deserves to lose his own by him against whom the attempt is made. And, therefore, since the Romans threatened us with this injury, it will undoubtedly turn to their own loss, if we can have but an opportunity of engaging with them.

"This is what the Britons universally desire; this is what we have promised us in the Sibylline prophesies, which expressly declare, that the Roman empire shall be obtained by three persons, natives of Britain. The oracle is fulfilled in two of them, since it is manifest (as your majesty observed) that those two celebrated princes, Belinus and Constantine, governed the Roman empire: and now you are the third to whom this supreme dignity is promised. Make haste, therefore, to receive what God makes no delay to give you; to subdue those who are ready to receive your yoke; and to advance us all, who for your advancement will spare neither limbs nor life. And that if you accomplish this, I myself will attend you in person with ten thousand men."

When Hoel concluded his speech, Augusel, king of Albania, declared his good affection to the cause after this manner.

"I am not able to express the joy that has transported

me, since my lord has declared to us his designs. For we seem to have done nothing by all our past wars with so many and potent princes, if the Romans and Germans can be suffered to enjoy peace, and we do not severely revenge on them the grievous oppressions which they formerly brought upon this country. But now, since we are at liberty to encounter them, I am overwhelmed with joy and eagerness of desire, to see a battle with them, when the blood of those cruel oppressors will be no less acceptable to me than a spring of water is to one who is parched with thirst. If I shall but live to see that day, how sweet will be the wounds which I shall then either receive or give? Nay, how sweet will be even death itself, when suffered in revenging the injuries done to our ancestors, in defending our liberties, and in promoting the glory of our king! Let us then begin with these poltroons, and spoil them of all their trophies, by making an entire conquest of them. And I for my share will add to the army two thousand horse, besides foot."

To the same effect spoke all the rest, and promised each of them their full quota of forces; so that besides those promised by the duke of Armorica, the number of men from the island of Britain alone was sixty thousand, all completely armed.

But the kings of the other islands, as they had not been accustomed to any cavalry, promised their quota of infantry; and, from the six provincial islands, viz. Ireland, Iceland, Gothland, the Orkneys, Norway, and Dacia, were reckoned a hundred and twenty thousand. From the duchies of Gaul, that is, of the Ruteni, the Portunians, the Etrusians, the Cenomanni, the Andegavians, and

Pictavians, were eighty thousand. From the twelve consulships of those who came along with Guerinus Carnotensis, twelve hundred. All together they made up a hundred and eighty-three thousand two hundred, besides foot which did not easily fall under number.

Preparing for War

King Arthur, seeing all unanimously ready for his service, ordered them to return back to their countries with speed, and get ready the forces which they had promised, and to hasten to the general rendezvous upon the kalends of August, at the mouth of the river Barba, that from thence they might advance with them to the borders of the Allobroges, to meet the Romans. Then he send word to the emperors by their ambassadors; that as to paying them tribute, he would in no wise obey their commands; and that the journey he was about to make to Rome, was not to stand the award of their sentence, but to demand of them what they had judicially decreed to demand of him. With this answer the ambassadors departed; and at the same time also departed all the kings and noblemen, to perform with all expedition the orders that had been given them.

Lucius Tiberius, on receiving this answer, by order of the senate published a decree, for the eastern kings to come with their forces, and assist in the conquest of Britain. In obedience to which their came in a very short time, Epistrophius, king of the Grecians; Mustensar, king of the Africans; Alifantinam, king of Spain; Hirtacius, king of the Parthians; Boccus, of the Medes; Sertorius, of Libya;

Teucer, king of Phrygia; Serses, king of the Itureans; Pandrasus, king of Egypt; Micipsa, king of Babylon; Polytetes, duke of Bithynia; Evander, of Syria; Aethion, of Boeotia; Hippolytus, of Crete, with the generals and nobility under them. Of the senatorial order also came Lucius Catellus, Marius Lepidus, Caius Metellus Cotta, Quintus Milvius Catulus, Quintus Carutius, and as many others as made up the number of forty thousand one hundred and sixty.

After the necessary dispositions were made, upon the kalends of August, they began their march towards Britain, which when Arthur had intelligence of, he committed the government of the kingdom to his nephew Modred, and queen Guanhumara, and marched with his army to Hamo's Port, where the wind stood fair for him.

But while he, surrounded with all his numerous fleet, was sailing joyfully with a brisk gale, it happened that about midnight he fell into a very sound sleep, and in a dream saw a bear flying in the air, at the noise of which all the shores trembled; also a terrible dragon flying from the west, which enlightened the country with the brightness of its eyes. When these two met, they began a dreadful fight; but the dragon with its fiery breath burned the bear which often assaulted him, and threw him down scorched to the ground.

Arthur upon this awaking, related his dream to those that stood about him, who took upon them to interpret it, and told him that the dragon signified himself, but the bear, some giant that should encounter with him; and that the fight portended the duel that would be between them, and the dragon's victory the same that would happen to himself. But Arthur conjectured it portended something else, and that the vision was applicable to himself and the emperor.

As soon as the morning after this night's sail appeared. They found themselves arrived at the mouth of the river Barba. And there they pitched their tents, to wait the arrival of the kings of the islands and the generals of the other provinces.

Arthur Slays a Giant

In the meantime Arthur had news brought to him, that a giant of monstrous size was come from the shores of Spain, and had forcibly taken away Helena, the niece of duke Hoel, from her guard, and fled with her to the top of that which is now called Michael's Mount; and that the soldiers of the country who pursued him were able to do nothing against him. For whether they attacked him by sea or land, he either overturned the ships with cast rocks, or killed them with several sorts of darts, besides many of them that he took and devoured half alive.

The next night, therefore, at the second hour, Arthur, taking along with him Caius the steward, and Bedver the butler, went out privately from the camp, and hastened towards the mountain. For being a man of undaunted courage, he did not care to lead his army against such monsters; both because he could in this manner animate his men by his own example, and also because he was alone sufficient to deal with them.

As soon as they came near the mountain, they saw a fire

burning upon the top of it, and another on a lesser mountain, that was not far from it. And being in doubt upon which of them the giant dwelt, they sent away Bedver to know the certainty of the matter. So he, finding a boat, sailed over in it first to the lesser mountain, to which he could in no other way have access, because it was situated in the sea. When he had begun to climb up to the top of it, he was at first frightened by a dismal howling cry of a woman from above, and imagined the monster to be there: but quickly rousing his courage, he drew his sword, and having reached the top, found nothing but the fire which he had before seen at a distance.

He discovered also a grave newly made, and an old woman weeping and howling by it, who at the sight of him instantly cried out in words interrupted with sighs, "O unhappy man, what misfortune brings you to this place? O the inexpressible tortures of death that you must suffer! I pity you, I pity you, because the detestable monster will this night destroy the flower of your youth. For that most wicked and odious giant, who brought the duke's niece, whom I have just now buried here, and me, her nurse, along with her into this mountain, will come and immediately murder you in a most cruel manner. O deplorable fate! This most illustrious princess, sinking under the fear her tender heart conceived, while the foul monster would have embraced her, fainted away and expired. And when he could not satiate his brutish lust upon her, who was the very soul, joy, and happiness of my life, being enraged at the disappointment of his bestial desire, he forcibly committed a rape upon me, who (let God and my old age witness) abhorred his embraces. Fly, dear sir, fly, for fear he may come, as he usually does, to lie with me, and finding you here most barbarously butcher you."

Bedver, moved at what she said, as much as it is possible for human nature to be, endeavoured with kind words to assuage her grief, and to comfort her with the promise of speedy help: and then returned back to Arthur, and gave him an account of what he had met with. Arthur very much lamented the damsel's sad fate, and ordered his companions to leave him to deal with him alone; unless there was an absolute necessity, and then they were to come in boldly to his assistance.

From hence they went directly to the next mountain, leaving their horses with their armour-bearers, and ascended to the top, Arthur leading the way. The deformed savage was then by the fire, with his face besmeared with the clotted blood of swine, part of which he already devoured, and was roasting the remainder upon spits by the fire.

But at the sight of them, whose appearance was a surprise to him, he hastened to his club, which two strong men could hardly lift from the ground. Upon this the king drew his sword, and guarding himself with his shield, ran with all his speed to prevent his getting it. But the other, who was not ignorant of his design, had by this time snatched it up, and gave the king such a terrible blow upon his shield, that he made the shores ring with the noise, and perfectly stunned the king's ears with it.

Arthur, fired with rage at this, lifted up his sword, and gave him a wound in the forehead, which was not indeed mortal, but yet such as made the blood gush out over his face and eyes, and so blinded him; for he had partly warded off the stroke from his forehead with his club, and prevented its being fatal. However, his loss of sight, by reason of the blood flowing over his eyes, made him exert himself with greater fury, and like an enraged boar against a hunting-spear, so did he rush in against Arthur's sword, and grasping him about the waist, forced him down upon his knees. But Arthur, nothing daunted, slipped out of his hands, and so exerted himself with his sword, that he gave the giant no respite till he had struck it up to the very back through his skull. At this the hideous monster raised a dreadful roar, and like an oak torn up from the roots by the winds, so did he make the ground resound with his fall.

Arthur, bursting out into a fit of laughter at the sight, commanded Bedver to cut of his head, and give it to one of the armour-bearers, who was to carry it to the camp, and there expose it to public view, but with orders for the spectators of this combat to keep silence.

He told them he had found none of so great strength, since he killed the giant Ritho, who had challenged him to fight, upon the mountain Aravius. This giant had made himself furs of the beards of kings he had killed, and had sent word to Arthur to carefully cut his beard and send it to him; and then, out of respect to his pre-eminence over other kings, his beard should have the honour of the principal place. But if he refused to do it, he challenged him to a duel, with this offer, that the conqueror should have the furs, and also the beard of the vanquished for a trophy of his victory. In his conflict, therefore, Arthur proved victorious, and took the beard and spoils of the giant: and, as he said before, he had met with none that could be compared to him for strength, till his last engagement.

After this victory, they returned at the second watch of the night to the camp with the head; to see which there was a great concourse of people, all extolling this wonderful exploit of Arthur, by which he had freed the country from a most destructive and voracious monster. But Hoel, in great grief for the loss of his niece, commanded a mausoleum to be built over her body in the mountain where she was buried, which, taking the damsel's name, is called Helena's Tomb to this day.

Battle with the Romans

As soon as all the forces were arrived where Arthur expected, he marched from thence to Augustodunum, where he supposed the general was. But when he came to the river Alba, he had intelligence brought him of his having encamped not far off, and that he was come with so vast an army, that he would not be able to withstand it. However, this did not deter him from pursuing his enterprise; but he pitched his camp upon the bank of the river, to facilitate the bringing up of his forces, and to secure his retreat, if there should be occasion, and sent Boso the consul of Oxford, and Guerinus Carnotensis, with his nephew Walgan, to Lucius Tiberius, requiring him either to return from the coasts of Gaul, or come the next day, that they might try their right to that country with their swords.

The retinue of young courtiers that attended Walgan,

highly rejoicing at this opportunity, were urgent with him to find some occasion for a quarrel in the commander's camp, that so they might engage the Romans. Accordingly they went to Lucius, and commanded him to retire out of Gaul, or hazard a battle the next day. But while he was answering them, that he was not come to retire, but to govern the country, there was present Caius Quintilianus, his nephew, who said that the Britons were better at boasting and threatening, than they were at fighting.

Walgan immediately took fire at this, and ran upon him with his drawn sword, wherewith he cut off his head, and then retreated speedily with his companions to their horses. The Romans, both horse and foot, pursued to revenge the loss of their countryman upon the ambassadors, who fled with great precipitation. But Guerinus Carnotensis, just as one of them was come up to him, rallied on a sudden, and with his lance struck at once through his armour and the very middle of his body, and aid him prostrate on the ground. The sight of this noble exploit raised the emulation of Boso of Oxford, who, wheeling about his horse, struck his lance into the throat of the first man he met with, and dismounted him mortally wounded.

In the meantime, Marcellus Mutius, with great eagerness to revenge Quintilian's death, was just upon the back of Walgan, and laid hold of him; which the other quickly obliged him to quit, by cleaving both his helmet and head to the breast with his sword. He also bade him, when he arrived at the infernal regions, tell the man he had killed in the camp, that in this manner the Britons showed their boasting and threatening. Then having reassembled his men, he encouraged them to despatch every one his pursuer in the same manner as he had done; which accordingly they did not fail to accomplish. Notwithstanding, the Romans continued their pursuit with lances and swords, wherewith they annoyed the others, though without slaughter or taking any prisoners.

But as they came near a certain wood, a party of six thousand Britons, who seeing the flight of the consuls, had hid themselves, to be in readiness for their assistance, sallied forth, and putting spurs to their horses, rent the air with loud shouts, and being well fenced with their shields, assaulted the Romans suddenly, and forced them to fly. And now it was the Britons' turn to pursue, which they did with better success, for they dismounted, killed, or took several of the enemy.

Petreius, the senator, upon this news, hastened to the assistance of his countrymen with ten thousand men, and compelled the Britons to retreat to the wood from whence they had sallied forth; though not without loss of his own men. For the Britons, being well acquainted with the ground, in their flight killed a great number of their pursuers. The Britons, thus giving ground, Hider, with another reinforcement of five thousand men, advanced with speed to sustain them; so that they again faced those upon whom they had turned their backs, and renewed the assault with great vigour. The Romans also stood their ground, and continued the fight with various success.

The great fault of the Britons was, that though they had been very eager to begin the fight, yet when begun they were less careful of the hazard they ran. Whereas the Romans were under better discipline, and had the advantage of a prudent commander, Petreius Cotta, to tell them where to advance, and where to give ground, and by these means did great injury to the enemy.

When Boso observed this, he drew off from the rest a large party of those whom he knew to be the stoutest men, and spoke to them after this manner: "Since we have begun this fight without Arthur's knowledge, we must take care that we be not defeated in the enterprise. For, if we should, we shall both very much endanger our men, and incur the king's high displeasure. Rouse up your courage, and follow me through the Roman squadrons, that with the favour of good fortune we may either kill or take Petreius prisoner."

With this they put spurs to their horses, and piercing through the enemies' thickest ranks, reached the place where Petrius was giving his commands. Boso hastily ran in upon him, and grasping him about the neck, fell with him to the ground, as he had intended. The Romans hereupon ran to his delivery, as did the Britons to Boso's assistance; which occasioned on both sides great slaughter, noise, and confusion, while one party strove to rescue their leader, and the other to keep him prisoner. So that this proved the sharpest part of the whole fight, and wherein their spears, swords, and arrows had the fullest employment.

At length, the Britons, joining in a close body, and sustaining patiently the assaults of the Romans, retired to the main body of their army with Petreius: which they had no sooner done, than they again attacked them, being now deprived of their leader, very much weakened, dispirited, and just beginning to flee. They, therefore, eagerly pursued, beat down, and killed several of them, and as soon as they had plundered them, pursued the rest: but they took the greatest number of them prisoners, being desirous to present them to the king.

Attempted Rescue

When they had at last sufficiently harassed them, they returned with their plunder and prisoners to the camp; where they gave an account of what had happened, and presented Petreius Cotta with the other prisoners before Arthur, with great joy for the victory. Arthur congratulated them upon it, and promised them advancement to greater honours, for behaving themselves so gallantly when he was absent from them.

Then he gave his command to some of his men, to conduct the prisoners the next day to Paris, and deliver them to be kept in custody there till further orders. The party that were to undertake this charge, he ordered to be conducted by Cador, Bedver, and the two consuls, Borellus and Richerius, with their servants, till they should be out of all fear of disturbance from the Romans.

But the Romans, happening to get intelligence of their design, at the command of their general chose out fifteen thousand men, who that night were to get before the others in their march, and rescue their fellow soldiers out of their hands. They were to be commanded by Vulteius Catellus and Quintus Carutius, senators, and also Evander, king of Syria, and Sertorius, king of Libya. Accordingly they began their march that very night, and possessed themselves of a place convenient for lying in ambuscade, through which they supposed the others would pass.

In the morning the Britons set forward along the same road with their prisoners, and were now approaching the place in perfect ignorance of the cunning stratagem of the enemy. No sooner had they entered it, than the Romans, to their great surprise, sprang forth and fell furiously upon them. Notwithstanding, the Britons, at length recovering from their consternation, assembled together, and prepared for a bold opposition, by appointing a party to guard the prisoners, and drawing out the rest in order of battle against the enemy. Richerius and Bedver had the command of the party that were set over the prisoners, but Cador, duke of Cornwall, and Borellus headed the others.

But all the Romans had made their sally without being placed in any order, and cared not to form themselves, that they might lose no time in the slaughter of the Britons, whom they saw busied in marshalling their troops, and preparing only for their defence. By this conduct the Britons were extremely weakened, and would have shamefully lost their prisoners, had not good fortune rendered them assistance. For Guitard, commander of he Pictavians, happened to get information of the designed stratagem, and was come up with three thousand men, by the help of which they at last got the advantage, and paid back the slaughter upon their insolent assailants.

Nevertheless, the loss which they sustained at the beginning of this action was very considerable. For they lost Borellus, the famous consul of the Cenomanni, in an encounter with Evander, king of Syria, who stuck his lance into his throat; besides four noblemen, viz. Hirelgas

Deperirus, Mauricius Cadorcanensis, Aliduc of Tintagel, and Hider his son, than who braver men were hardly to be found.

But yet neither did this loss dispirit the Britons, but rather made them more resolute to keep the prisoners, and kill the enemy. The Romans, now finding themselves unable to maintain the fight any longer, suddenly quitted the field, and made towards their camp; but were pursued with slaughter by the Britons, who also took many of them, and allowed them no respite till they had killed Vulteius Catellus and Evander, king of Syria, and wholly dispersed the rest. After which they sent away their former prisoners to Paris, whither they were to conduct them, and returned back with those newly taken to the king; to whom they gave great hopes of a complete conquest of their enemies, since very few of the great number that came against them had met with any success.

Arthur Prepares for Battle

These repeated disasters wrought no small disturbance in the mind of Lucius Tiberius, and made him hesitate whether to bring it to a general battle with Arthur, or to retire into Augustodunum, and stay till the emperor Leo with his forces could come to his assistance. At length, giving way to his fears, he entered Lengria with his army, intending to reach the other city the night following.

Arthur, finding this, and being desirous to get before him in his march, left the city on the left hand, and the same night entered a certain valley called Suesia, through which Lucius was to pass. There he divided his men into several bodies, commanding one legion, over which Morvid, consul of Gloucester, was appointed general, to wait close by, that he might retreat to them if there should be occasion, and from thence rally his broken forces for a second battle. The rest he divided into seven parts, in each of which he placed five thousand five hundred and fifty-five men, all completely armed. Hr also appointed different stations to his horse and foot, and gave command that just as the foot should advance to the attack, the horse, keeping close together in their ranks, should at the same moment march up obliquely, and endeavour to put the enemy into disorder.

The companies of foot were, after the British manner, drawn out into a square, with a right and left wing, under the command of Augusel, king of Albanis, and Cador, duke of Cornwall; the one presiding over the right wing, the other over the left. Over another party were placed the two famous consuls, Guerinus of Chartres and Boso of Richiden, called in the Saxon tongue Oxineford; over a third were Aschillius, king of the Dacians, and Lot, king of the Norwegians; the fourth being commanded by Hoel, duke of the Armoricans, and Walgan, the king's nephew. After these were four other parties placed in the rear; the first commanded by Caius the steward, and Bedver the butler; the second by Holdin, duke of the Ruteni, and Guitard of the Pictavians; the third by Vigenis of Legecester, Jonathal of Dorchester, and Cursalem of Caicester; the fourth by Urtgennius of Bath.

Behind all these, Arthur, for himself and the legion that was to attend near him, made choice of a place, where he set up a golden dragon for a standard, whither the wounded or fatigued might in case of necessity retreat, as into their camp. The legion that was with him consisted of six thousand six hundred and sixty-six men.

After he had thus placed them all in their stations, he made the following speech to his soldiers: —

"My brave countrymen, who have made Britain the mistress of thirty kingdoms, I congratulate you on your noble exploit which to me is proof that your valour is so far from being impaired, that it is rather increased. Though you have been five years without exercise, wherein the softening pleasures of an easy life had a greater share of your time than the use of arms; yet all this has not made you degenerate from your natural bravery, which you have shown in forcing the Romans to flee.

"The pride of their leaders has animated them to attempt the invasion of your liberties. They have tried you in battle, with numbers superior to yours, and have not been able to stand before you; but have basely withdrawn themselves into that city, from which they are now ready to march out, and to pass through this valley in their way to Augustodunum; so that you may have an opportunity of falling upon them unawares like a flock of sheep. Certainly they expected to find in you the cowardice of the Eastern nations, when they thought to make your country tributary, and you their slaves. What, have they never heard of your wars, with the Dacians, Norwegians, and princes of the Gauls, whom you reduced under my power, and freed from their shameful yoke? We, then, that have had success in a greater war, need not doubt of it in a less, if we do but endeavour with the same spirit to vanquish these poltroons. You shall want no rewards of honour, if as faithful soldiers you do but strictly obey my commands. For as soon as we have routed them, we will march straight to Rome, and take it: and then all the gold, silver, palaces, towers, towns, cities, and other riches of the vanquished shall be yours."

He had hardly done speaking before they all with one voice declared, that they were ready to suffer death, rather than quit the field while he had life.

Lucius Prepares for Battle

But Lucius Tiberius, discovering the designs that were formed against him, would not flee, as he had at first intended, but taking new courage, resolved to march to the same valley against them; and calling together his principal commanders, spoke to them in these words:—

"Venerable fathers, to whose empire both the Eastern and Western kingdoms owe obedience, remember the virtues of your ancestors, who were not afraid to shed their blood, when the vanquishing of the enemies of the commonwealth required it; but to leave an example of their courage and military virtues to their posterity, behaved themselves in all battles with the contempt of death, as if God had given them some security against it. By this conduct they often triumphed, and by triumphing escaped death. Such was the reward of their virtue from Divine Providence, which overrules all events. This increase of the commonwealth, and of their own valour was owing to this; and all those virtues that usually adorn the great, as integrity, honour, and munificence, flourishing a long time in them, raised them and their posterity to the empire of the whole world. Let their noble examples animate you: rouse up the spirit of the ancient Romans, and be not afraid to march out against our enemies that are lying in ambush before us in the valley, but boldly with your swords demand of them your just rights.

"Do not think that I retired into this city for fear of engaging with them; but I thought that, as their pursuit of us was rash and foolish, so we might hence on a sudden intercept them in it, and by dividing their main body make a great slaughter of them. But now, since they have altered the measures which we supposed they had taken, let us also alter ours. Let us go in quest of them and bravely fall upon them; or if they shall happen to have the advantage in the beginning of the battle, let us only stand our ground during the fury of their first assault, and the victory will undoubtedly be ours; for in many battles this manner of conduct has been attended with victory."

As soon as he had made an end of speaking these and other things, they all declared their assent, promised with an oath to stand by him, and hastened to arm themselves. Which when they had done, they marched out of Lengriae to the valley where Arthur had drawn out his forces in order of battle. Then they also began to marshall their army, which they divided into twelve companies, and according to the Roman manner of battle, drew out each company in the form of a wedge, consisting of six thousand six hundred and sixty six men.

Each company also had its respective leaders, who were to give direction when to advance, or when to be on the defensive. One of them was headed by Lucius Catellus the senator, and Alifantinam, king of Spain; another by Hirtacius, king of the Parthians, and Marius Lepidus, a senator. These four companies were placed in front of the army. In the rear of these were four others, whereof one was commanded by Serses, king of the Itureans; another by Pandrasus, king of Egypt; a third by Polytetes, duke of Bithynia; a fourth by Teucer, duke of Phrygia. And again behind all these four others, whereof the commanders were Quintus Carucius, a senator, Laelius Ostiensis, Sulpitius Subuculus, and Mauricius Sylvanus.

As for the general himself, he was sometimes in one place, sometimes in another, to encourage and direct as there should be occasion. For a standard he ordered a golden eagle to be firmly set up in the centre, for his men to repair to when they should happen to be separated from their company.

The Britons Battle the Romans

And now the Britons and Romans stood presenting their arms at one another; when forthwith at the sound of trumpets, the company that was headed by the king of Spain and Lucius Catellus, boldly rushed forward against that which the king of Scotland and duke of Cornwall led, but were not able to make the least breach in their firm ranks. So that while these stood their ground, up came Guerinus and Boso with a body of horse upon their full speed, broke through the party that began the assault, and met with another which the king of the Parthians was leading up against Aschillius, king of Dacia.

After this first onset, there followed a general engagement of both armies with great violence, and several breaches were made on each side. The shouts, the slaughter, the quantity of blood spilled, and the agonies of the dying, made a dreadful scene of horror.

At first, the Britons sustained a great loss, by having Bedver the butler killed, and Caius the steward mortally wounded. For, as Bedver met Boccus, king of the Medes, he fell dead by a stab of his lance amidst the enemies' troops. And Caius, in endeavouring to revenge his death, was surrounded by the Median troops, and there received a mortal wound; yet as a brave soldier he opened himself a way with the wing which he led, killed and dispersed the Medes, and would have made a safe retreat with all his men, had he not met the king of Libya with the forces under him, who put his whole company into disorder; yet not so great, but that he was still able to get off with a few, and flee with Bedver's corpse to the golden dragon.

The Neustrians grievously lamented the sight of their leader's mangled body; and so did the Andegavians, when they beheld their consul wounded. But there was now no room for complaints, for the furious and bloody shocks of both armies made it necessary to provide for their own defence.

Therefore Hirelgas, the nephew of Bedver, being extremely enraged at his death, called up to him three hundred men, and like a wild boar amongst a pack of dogs, broke through the enemies' ranks with his horse, making towards the place where he had seen the standard of the king of the Medes; little regarding what might befall him, if he could but revenge the loss of his uncle. At length he reached the place, killed the king, brought off his body to his companions, and laid it by that of his uncle, where he mangled it in the same manner. Then calling with a loud voice to his countrymen, he animated their troops, and vehemently pressed them to exert themselves to the utmost, now that their spirits were raised, and the enemy disheartened; and especially as they had the advantage of them in being placed in better order, and so might the more grievously annoy them.

Encouraged with this exhortation, they began a general assault upon the enemy, which was attended with a terrible slaughter on both sides. For on the part of the Romans, besides many others, fell Alifantinam, king of Spain, Micipsa of Babylon, as also Quintus Milvius and Marius Lepidus, senators. On the part of the Britons, Holdin, king of the Ruteni, Loedegarius of Bolonia, and three consuls of Britain, Cursalem of Caicester, Galluc of Salisbury, and Urtgennius of Bath. So that the troops which they commanded, being extremely weakened, retreated till they came to the army of the Armorican Britons, commanded by Hoel and Walgan. But these, being inflamed at the retreat of their friends, encouraged them to stand their ground, and caused them with the help of their own forces to put their pursuers to flight. When they continued this pursuit, they beat down and killed several of them, and gave them no respite, till they came to the general's troop; who, seeing the distress of his companions, hastened to their assistance.

And now in this latter encounter the Britons were

worsted, with the loss of Kimarcoc, consul of Trigeria, and two thousand men with him; besides three famous noblemen, Richomarcus, Bloccovius, and Jagivius of Bodloan, who, had they but enjoyed the dignity of princes, would have been celebrated for their valour through all succeeding ages. For, during this assault which they made in conjunction with Hoel and Walgan, there was not an enemy within their reach that could escape the fury of their sword or lance. But upon their falling in among Lucius's party, they were surrounded by them, and suffered the same fate with the consul and the other men.

The loss of these men made those matchless heroes, Hoel and Walgan, much more eager to assault the general's ranks. and to try on all sides where to make the greatest impression. But Walgan, whose valour was never to be foiled, endeavoured to gain access to Lucius himself; that he might encounter him, and with this view beat down and killed all that stood in his way. And Hoel, not inferior to him, did no less service in another part, by spiriting up his men, and giving and receiving blows among the enemy with the same undaunted courage. It was hard to determine, which of them was the stoutest soldier.

But Walgan, by forcing his way through the enemy's troops, as we said before, found at last (what he had wished for) access to the general, and immediately encountered him. Lucius, being then in the flower of his youth, and a person of great courage and vigour, desired nothing more than to engage with such a one as might put his strength to its full trial. Putting himself, therefore, into a posture of defence, he received Walgan with joy, and was not a little proud to try his courage with one of whom he had heard such great things. The fight continued between them a long time, with great force of blows, and no less dexterity in warding them off, each being resolved upon the other's destruction.

Arthur's Victory

During this sharp conflict between them, the Romans, on a sudden, recovering their courage, made an assault upon the Armoricans, and having relieved their general, repulsed Hoel and Walgan, with their troops, till they found themselves unawares met by Arthur and the forces under him. For he, hearing of the slaughter that was a little before made of his men, had speedily advanced with his legion, and drawing out his Caliburn, spoke to them, with a loud voice, after this manner:

"What are you doing, soldiers? Will you suffer these effeminate wretches to escape? Let not one of them get off alive. Remember the force of your arms, that have reduced thirty kingdoms under my subjection. Remember your ancestors, whom the Romans, when at the height of their power, made tributary. Remember your liberties, which these pitiful fellows, that are much your inferiors, attempt to deprive you of. Let none of them escape alive. What are you doing?"

With these expostulations, he rushed upon the enemy, made terrible havoc among them, and not a man did he meet but at one blow he laid either him or his horse dead upon the ground. They, therefore, in astonishment fled from him, as a flock of sheep from a fierce lion, whom raging hunger provokes to devour whatever happens to come near him. Their arms were no manner of protection from them against the force with which this valiant prince wielded his Caliburn. Two kings, Sertorius of Libya, and Polyetes of Bithynia, unfortunately felt its fury, and had their heads cut off by it.

The Britons, when they saw the king performing such wonders, took courage again. With one consent they assaulted the Romans, kept close together in their ranks, and while they assailed the foot in one part, endeavoured to beat down and pierce through the horse in another. Notwithstanding, the Romans made a brave defence, and at the instigation of Lucius laboured to pay back their slaughter upon the Britons.

The eagerness and force that were now shown on both sides were as great as if it was the beginning of the battle. Arthur continued to do great execution with his own hand, and encouraged the Britons to maintain the fight, as Lucius Tiberius did the Romans, and made them perform many memorable exploits. He himself, in the meantime, was very active in going from place to place, and suffered none to escape with life that happened to come within the reach of his sword or lance. The slaughter that was now made on both sides was very dreadful, and the turns of fortune various, sometimes the Britons prevailing, sometimes the Romans.

At last, while this sharp dispute continued Morvid, consul of Gloucester, with his legion, which, as we said before, was placed between the hills, came up with speed upon the rear of the enemy, and to their great surprise assaulted, broke through, and dispersed them with great slaughter. This last and decisive blow proved fatal to many thousands of Romans, and even to the general Lucius himself, who was killed among the crowds with a lance by an unknown hand. But the Britons, by long maintaining the fight, at last with great difficulty gained the victory.

After the Battle

The Romans, being now, therefore, dispersed, betook themselves through fear, some to the by-ways and woods, some to the cities and towns, and all other places, where they could be most safe; but were either killed or taken and plundered by the Britons who pursued: so that great part of them voluntarily and shamefully held forth their hands, to receive their chains, in order to prolong for a while a wretched life. In all which the justice of Divine Providence was very visible, considering how unjustly the ancestors of the Britons were formerly invaded and harassed by those of the Romans; and that these stood only in defence of that liberty, which the others would have deprived them of; and refused the tribute, which the others had no right to demand.

Arthur, after he had completed his victory, gave orders for separating the bodies of his nobility from those of the enemy, and preparing a pompous funeral for them; and that, when ready, they should be carried to the abbeys of their respective countries, there to be honourably buried.

But Bedver the butler was, with great lamentation of the Neustrians, carried to his own city Bajocae, which Bedver the first, his great grandfather, had built. There he was, with great solemnity, laid close by the wall, in a burying-place on the south side of the city. But Caius was carried, grievously wounded to Chinon, a town which he had himself built, where in a short time he died of his wounds, and was buried, as became a duke of Andegavia, in a convent of hermits, which was in a wood not far from the town. Also Holdin, duke of Ruteni, was carried to Flanders, and buried in his own city Terivana.

The other consuls and noblemen were conveyed to the neighbouring abbeys, according to Arthur's orders. Out of great clemency, also, he ordered the country people to take care of the burial of the enemy, and to carry the body of Lucius to the senate, and tell them, that was the only tribute which Britain ought to pay them.

Chapter 8: The Death of Arthur

Modred's Treachery

After this he stayed in those parts till the next winter was over, and employed his time in reducing the cities of the Allobroges. But at the beginning of the following summer, as he was on his march towards Rome, and was beginning to pass the Alps, he had news brought to him that his nephew Modred, to whose care he had entrusted Britain, had by tyrannical and treasonable practices set the crown upon his own head; and that queen Guanhumara, in violation of her first marriage, had wickedly married him.

Of the matter now to be treated of, most noble consul, Geoffrey of Monmouth shall be silent; but will, nevertheless, though in a mean style, briefly relate what he found in the British book above mentioned, and heard from that most learned historian, Walter, archdeacon of

Oxford, concerning the wars which this renowned king, upon this return to Britain after this victory, waged against his nephew.

As soon, therefore, as the report, of this flagrant wickedness reached him, he immediately desisted from his enterprise against Leo, king of the Romans; and having sent away Hoel, duke of the Armoricans, with the army of Gaul, to restore peace in those parts, returned back with speed to Britain, attended only by the kings of the islands, and their armies.

But the wicked traitor, Modred, had sent Cheldric, the Saxon leader, into Germany, there to raise all the forces he could find, and return with all speed: and in consideration of this service, had promised him all that part of the island, which reaches from the Humber to Scotland, and whatever Hengist and Horsa had possessed of Kent in the time of Vortigern. So that he, in obedience to his commands, had arrived with eight hundred ships filled with pagan soldiers, and had entered into a covenant to obey the traitor as his sovereign; who had also drawn to his assistance the Scots, Picts, Irish, and all others whom he knew to be enemies of his uncle.

His whole army, taking pagans and Christians together, amounted to eighty thousand men; and with the help of whom he met Arthur just after his landing at the port of Rutupi, and joining battle with him, made a very great slaughter of his men. For the same day fell Augusel, king of Albania, and Walgan, the king's nephew, with innumerable others. Augusel was succeeded in his kingdom by Eventus, his brother Urian's son, who afterwards performed many famous exploits in those wars.

After they had at last, with much difficulty, got ashore, they paid back the slaughter, and put Modred and his army to flight. For, by long practice in war, they had learned an excellent way of ordering their forces; which was so managed, that while their foot were employed wither in an assault or upon the defensive, the horse would come in at full speed obliquely, break through the enemy's ranks, and so force them to flee.

Nevertheless, the perjured usurper got his forces together again, and the night following entered Winchester. As soon as queen Guanhumara heard this, she immediately, despairing of success, fled from York to the City of Legions, where she resolved to live a chaste life among the nuns in the church of Julius the Martyr, and entered herself one of their order.

Arthur's Last Battle

But Arthur, whose anger was now much more inflamed, upon the loss of so many hundreds of fellow soldiers, after he had buried his slain, went on the third day to the city, and there besieged the traitor, who, notwithstanding, was unwilling to desist from his enterprise, but used all methods to encourage his adherents, and marching out with his troops prepared to fight his uncle.

In the battle that followed hereupon, great numbers lost their lives on both sides; but at last Modred's army suffered most, so that he was forced to quit the field shamefully. From hence he made a precipitate flight, and, without taking any care for the burial of his slain, marched

139

in haste towards Cornwall. Arthur, being inwardly grieved that he should so often escape, forthwith pursued him into that country as far as the river Cambula, where the other was expecting his coming.

And Modred, as he was the boldest of men, and always the quickest at making an attack, immediately placed his troops in order, resolving either to conquer or to die, rather than continue his flight any longer. He had yet remaining with him sixty thousand men, out of whom he composed three bodies, which contained each of them six thousand six hundred and sixty six men: but all the rest he joined in one body; and having assigned to each of the other parties their leaders, he took the command of this upon himself. After he had made this disposition of forces, he endeavoured to animate them, and promised them the estates of their enemies if they came off with victory.

Arthur, on the other side, also marshalled his army, which he divided into nine square companies, with a right and left wing; and having appointed to each of them their commanders, exhorted them to make a total rout of those robbers and perjured villains, who, being brought over into the island from foreign countries at the instance of the arch-traitor, were attempting to rob them of all their honours. He likewise told them that a mixed army composed of barbarous people of so many different countries, and who were all raw soldiers and inex-perienced in war, would never be able to stand against such brave veteran troops as they were, provided they did their duty.

After this encouragement given by each general to his fellow soldiers, the battle on a sudden began with great fury; wherein it would be both grievous and tedious to relate the slaughter, the cruel havoc, and the excess of fury that was to be seen on both sides. In this manner they spent a good part of the day, till Arthur at last made a push with his company, consisting of six thousand six hundred and sixty-six men, against that in which he knew Modred was; and having opened a way with their swords, they pierced quite through it, and made a grievous slaughter. For in this assault fell the wicked traitor himself, and many thousands with him.

But notwithstanding the loss of him, the rest did not flee, but running together from all parts of the field maintained their ground with undaunted courage. The fight now grew more furious than ever, and proved fatal to almost all their commanders and their forces. For on Modred's side fell Cheldric, Elasius, Egbrict, and Bunignus, Saxons; Gillapatric, Gillamor, Gistafel, and Gallarius, Irish; also the Scots and Picts, with almost all their leaders: on Arthur's side, Olbrict, king of Norway; Aschillius, king of Dacia; Cador Limenic Cassibellaun, with many thousands of others, as well Britons as foreigners, that he had brought with him.

And even the renowned king Arthur himself was mortally wounded; and being carried thence to the isle of Avallon to be cured of his wounds, he gave up the crown of Britain to his kinsman Constantine, the son of Cador, duke of Cornwall, in the five hundred and forty-second year of our Lord's incarnation.

Appendix: Avalon

Avalon is one of the mysteries of Geoffrey's History. The History mentions that Arthur's sword, Caliburn, was made in Avallon (as Geoffrey spells it) and that Arthur was taken there after he was mortally wounded, but it says nothing more about Avalon.

Geoffrey does describe Avalon in his poem "Vita Merlini" (The Life of Merlin). He calls it the Isle of Apples in this poem, while he calls it the Isle of Avallon in the History. The name Avalon probably comes from the British word for apple, afal, which is aval in Welsh. The Isle of Apples and the Isle of Avalon are clearly the same place, because they are where Arthur is taken after being mortally wounded.

This excerpt from "The Life of Merlin" tells us more about Avalon and about Arthur's being taken there to be healed. It also introduces Morgen, who will become known as Morgan le Fay in later Arthurian romances.

From Vita Merlini[9]

The island of apples which men call "The Fortunate Isle" gets its name from the fact that it produces all things of itself; the fields there have no need of the ploughs of the farmers and all cultivation is lacking except what nature provides. Of its own accord it produces grain and grapes, and apple trees grow in its woods from the close-clipped grass. The ground of its own accord produces everything instead of merely grass, and people live there a hundred years or more. There nine sisters rule by a pleasing set of laws those who come to them from our country.

She who is first of them is more skilled in the healing art, and excels her sisters in the beauty of her person. Morgen is her name, and she has learned what useful properties all the herbs contain, so that she can cure sick bodies. She also knows an art by which to change her shape, and to cleave the air on new wings like Daedalus; when she wishes she is at Brest, Chartres, or Pavia, 49and when she will she slips down from the air onto your shores. And men say that she has taught mathematics to her sisters, Moronoe, Mazoe, Gliten, Glitonea, Gliton, Tyronoe, Thitis; Thitis best known for her cither.

Thither after the battle of Camlan we took the wounded Arthur, guided by Barinthus 50 to whom the waters and the stars of heaven were well known. With him steering the ship we arrived there with the prince, and Morgen received it with fitting honour, and in her chamber she

---

[9] Geoffrey of Monmouth's poem is in Latin. This excerpt is from the 1925 translation by John Jay Parry.

placed the king on a golden bed and with her own hand she uncovered his honourable wound and gazed at it for a long time.

At length she said that health could be restored to him if he stayed with her for a long time and made use of her healing art. Rejoicing, therefore, we entrusted the king to her and returning spread our sails to the favouring winds."

CPSIA information can be obtained
at www.ICGtesting.com
Printed in the USA
LVHW090257040620
657329LV00031B/100